CRAFT TECHNIQUES FOR TRADITIONAL BUILDINGS

CRAFT TECHNIQUES FOR TRADITIONAL BUILDINGS

Adela Wright RIBA

B T Batsford Ltd London

First published 1991

Typeset by Latimer Trend & Company Ltd, Plymouth
and printed in Great Britain by
The Bath Press, Bath

Published by B T Batsford Ltd
4 Fitzhardinge Street, London W1H 0AH

A CIP catalogue record for this book is
available from the British Library

ISBN 0 7134 6418 6

To George, Tim, Hilary and Antonia

The research for this work has been made possible by a grant from The Architects' Registration Council of the United Kingdom and the Leverhulme Trust

CONTENTS

PART II ROOFING

ACKNOWLEDGMENT

I acknowledge, with grateful thanks, the debt I owe for the generous help offered by all those mentioned in the text (see also separate acknowledgments following relevant chapters). It must be stressed that I alone am responsible for any errors in conclusions drawn from views expressed. I should also stress that where I express views I do so entirely independently of my connection with the Society for the Protection of Ancient Buildings.

I offer special thanks to Anthony Foxell for the many hours spent printing my photographs and above all to my husband, George, for all his help and impatience.

For the cover photograph I acknowledge Gillian Darley. I am deeply indebted to The Architects' Registration Council of the United Kingdom and The Leverhulme Trust for making reseach for this work possible.

Sevenoaks 1990

A W

General introduction

We live in a country that contains a wide range of some of the finest and most interesting vernacular buildings in the world, yet the pattern of caring for them is such that we turn, far too often, to the latest technological solutions, and use unsuitable modern building products, instead of seeking help from those who understand these structures. Craftsmen, with a lifetime of knowledge acquired under the old cultures, are still to be found; they possess traditional skills that have been developed, perfected and handed down for generations – the timeless way of building.

Unsympathetic methods of repair, together with the all too common desire to make an old building more perfect by renewing instead of repairing, has done much to hasten the decay or destruction of our much-loved old building stock. The Victorian cult of medievalism which induced a romantic longing to recreate the past lingers on. More old buildings were lost through restoration than by any other means during the Victorian era. It was against this backcloth that in 1877 William Morris founded the Society for the Protection of Ancient Buildings. The Manifesto of its foundation made a plea to all those on whom the care of old buildings rested 'to put protection in the place of restoration, to stave off decay by daily care, to prop a perilous wall or mend a leaky roof by such means as are obviously meant for support or covering, and show no pretence of other art, and otherwise to resist all tampering with either the fabric or ornament of the building as it stands . . . in fine, to treat our ancient buildings as monuments of a bygone art, created by bygone manners, that modern art cannot meddle with without destroying'.

The old craftsman understood this philosophy. With the inherent knowledge of his special craft he respected the simplicity of an old building; he was aware of the limitations of the material of which it was built; he recognized the risks involved in introducing new techniques or new materials that were incompatible with the old.

In recent decades traditional techniques have been largely disregarded; but there has been a fresh impetus of late to realize the importance of the original workmanship in vernacular buildings, to interpret the nature of the building fabric and, above all, to appreciate the craftsman's approach to conservative repair.

Published information on many of the old repair techniques is often scant or controversial. Oral communication can be more accurate, and is usually more explicit in detail, than the printed source. Craftsmen, with their practical knowledge, seldom write about their work but are usually pleased to talk about it and discuss information handed down from others of older standing. These men have invaluable links with the great building traditions of the Middle Ages.

The disappearance of traditional skills poses an increasing threat to the character of vernacular buildings. It was with this thought in mind that the author set out to search for building craftsmen, or others with a knowledge of building with some of the less familiar materials. If old skills can be perpetuated not only will our old buildings benefit but also there appears to be little reason why we should not, when building new structures, turn once again to some of those neglected materials that provided interest and variety to our vernacular heritage.

Part I
WALLING

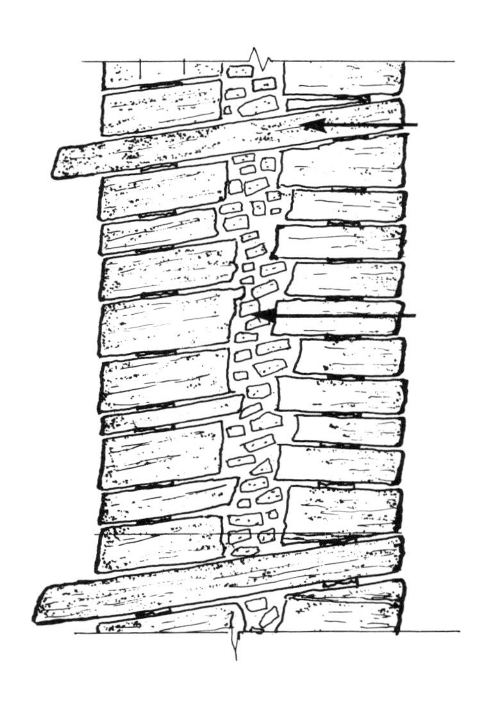

1 EARTH WALLING

Mud as a walling material has claim to be the oldest and most widely used form of vernacular construction in the world. In Britain the tradition of building with unbaked earth was widespread until the nineteenth century with the greatest concentration in South West England, East Anglia and in parts of the Midlands. During the Victorian period earth walls became unfashionable and some of the street-facing elevations of houses so built were refaced with brick, stone or flint. Many were also disguised behind coats of plaster.

The houses are pleasing to look at and their excellent thermal and sound insulating properties make them comfortable to live in. Mud was also used for farm buildings and boundary walls; animals fared well in the warm, even temperatures, and garden walls

1.1 A clay/mud cottage near Moorhouse on the Solway Plain. The thin layers of mud are interspersed with straw

1.2 Detail of the walling shown in figure **1.1**

retained heat from the sun which protected fruit from the frost. Construction costs were minimal and there was an almost inexhaustible supply of raw material. Mud was normally dug from the site although road scrapings were sometimes used. Relatively unskilled labour was required to build a wall and cottagers would often carry out the work themselves.

The disadvantages were that walls were easily eroded by water if not maintained. They needed a good overhang at the eaves to throw water clear of the walls, and a plinth of stone, brick or flint to counteract rising damp and to act as a splashback. An old Devon maxim on cob walls says 'gie un a gude hat and pair of buts an' ee'l last for ever'. Animals and insects were, and still are, a problem; rats and bees burrow into walls and cattle rub against farm buildings.

The main methods of construction in Britain were:

(a) *Cob:* the mud and straw mix was built up in horizontal layers and the sides were then pared down. (See chapter 3.)

(b) *Pisé:* rammed earth was built up in courses between movable wooden shutters. (See chapter 6.)

(c) *Cob lump, clay lump* or *clay bat:* compressed earth was set in wooden moulds and left to dry in the sun before being used for building. (See chapter 2.)

(d) *Wattle and daub infill panels to timber-framed structures:* the mud/straw mix was pressed into both sides of the wattle panels. (See chapter 15.)

1.3 Earth, clay, wychert and chalk conglomerate walling

2 CLAY LUMP

2.1 and **2.2** Clay lump buildings at Great Hockham, Norfolk

2.2

Most of the surviving clay lump walls of houses, barns and boundary walls, are in Suffolk, Norfolk, Cambridgeshire or northern Essex. They appear to date mainly from the late eighteenth century to the mid-nineteenth century. But evidence suggests that there may be a number of earlier buildings of either lump or unshuttered clay construction. They are not always easy to recognize for many are disguised behind brick or flint façades or thick coats of render.

The houses are comfortable to live in and easy and economical to build; two men can make about 400 blocks in a day. Shrinkage can be a problem but settlement is rare as a lump wall will adjust to movement.* The walling will tolerate a certain amount of water but is vulnerable to the destructive action of frost and must therefore be protected with a render.

A clay lump block is similar in concept to, but larger than, an unfired brick (adobe).

* Mr CE Smith of Great Hockham.

2.3 Garboldisham, Norfolk. Erosion due to the loss of the protective coping and render

2.4 Close up view of the wall shown in figure **2.3**

The clay is mixed with straw and formed into blocks by pressing the mix into wooden moulds that have neither bases nor tops. The mix is left in the sun to dry before construction takes place, then laid in a mortar of puddled clay and bonded in the same way as brickwork.

The lumps are made from the boulder clay of unstratified glacial deposits left behind after the melting of an ice sheet; the fine rock flour formed by the grinding together of rocks makes a durable material for the construction of walls.

Clay lump at Great Hockham, Norfolk

Mr Clarence Edward Smith is one of the last remaining builders to have had first-hand experience of building with clay lump using traditional techniques. He has lived all his life at Great Hockham and dwelt in a clay lump house from 1917 to 1945. He has repaired many of the buildings of the district. His father was a builder from 1886 by which time the building of new houses in clay lump was already on the decline. 'Building with clay lump', says Mr Smith, 'was something that was handed down from father to son, father to son, and if you didn't keep it in your head those secrets went to the grave.'

Great Hockham is a picturesque village; Mr Smith believes that an older hamlet was moved to the present site soon after the Black Death; he says that most of the earliest houses are either clay lump or wattle and daub. Many have been faced with brick or flint. The majority of the roofs were thatched until the First World War.

Preparation of clay

Mr Smith describes the local clay as 'nice pliable stuff and easy to work with; elsewhere clays are sticky and less durable'. He cites an instance where a local building firm built some houses at St Albans in 1920 using clay obtained close to the building site; the clay proved unsuitable and the houses were short lived.

Clay around Great Hockham is 24 to 36 in.

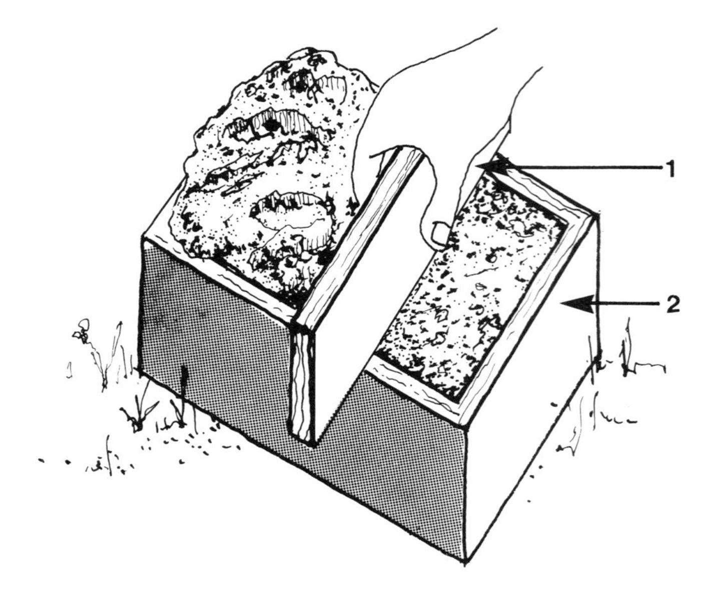

2.5 A clay lump block
1 A section of wood to level the clay
2 A timber mould without a base or top

(609 to 914 mm) down. 'They liked to dig in autumn, throw water on and leave it to use in the spring. It was best to let the frost and winter weather get to it to break it up. But they did not always leave it.

'The old clay makers would dig a pit, pond or pool about 36 in. [914 mm] down and the clay was thrown into this wet morass. They would also add short straw or *quicks* – a water grass.* When farmers cleaned the land in spring they would carry heaps of quicks to the builders. There was nothing stronger than this plant for reinforcement; the long roots were like bands of wire. You wouldn't find straw in the older buildings. I can only assume that three or four hundred years ago straw was more valuable, but it was sometimes used in external plaster. The clay would be kneaded by the feet of a horse walking round and round, tethered to a central pole, perhaps under the watchful eye of a man to keep him going round – great cruelty really – the poor beasts did not like the sticky clay hanging to their legs.

'I don't think that they added anything else to the clay in my father's time; although you do sometimes see bits of chalk in it. However, the exterior plaster was more chalky as though marl or lime had been put into it.

'The many ponds in the village are the sites from where the clay was dug.

Making the blocks

'The clay was put into wooden boxes with a shovel; some might have used plastering trowels to level off the top face but a straight piece of wood was more usual. The box had no base and it was placed on the grass or soil. A box of 9 × 6 × 12 in. [225 × 150 × 300 mm] was the standard size but other sizes were used up to 24 × 6 × 9 in. [600 × 150 × 225 mm].

'As soon as the clay was hard enough, which might be the following day, they would lift the mould off and let the block dry for a

* *Quitch* – couch grass . . . supposed to be related to *cwic*. QUICK with reference to the vitality of the grass. *The Oxford Dictionary of English Etymology*.

week or a fortnight. It didn't matter if the tops of the blocks were not even. As soon as they were dry enough to handle they were stacked honeycomb fashion, to allow the air to circulate, on a bed of levelled sand.

'They would use the same clay for bedding the blocks but there were no quicks or straw in this.

Building a house

'A house took more than a year to build in those days. It was easier to build with clay lump than with brick in freezing weather; you can put anti-freeze in the water when building with brick but the sand will still freeze. However, you did cover a lump wall at night with scaffolding boards or by sacking down. You also put scaffolding boards on top of the walls during the day to protect them from rain.

'Most plinth foundations were flint which were built up to a height of about 24 in. [600 mm] above the ground. Although there were bricks to be bought, the flints could be picked up from the roadside or from local stone pits. We laid them "flint touch flint" with no joint. The house that I lived in had no foundations: it consisted of lime, cobble and sand under a brick plinth and there have never been any settlement cracks. Very few settlement cracks were ever found in clay lump buildings as they were soft and gave with movement.

'Walls were usually 9 in. [225 mm] thick, ie the width of one block. I have seen walls 24 in. [600 mm] thick and also three-storey

2.6 Rendered clay lump houses at Great Hockham. Early twentieth century

2.7 Garboldisham, Norfolk. The construction of the gable was simplified by using another material. This was a common practice in minor buildings

houses but these may have been packed clay as there were no signs of joints. Some lump walls were reduced to a thickness of 6 in. [150 mm] in gable walls; the explanation offered was that this would reduce the weight.

'There were no damp-proof courses. There may have been some rising damp but nobody worried about it; they were warm houses. For the better houses they would encase the clay lump in red brick. The lump walls were left to settle for two years. The bricks were then tied to the lumps with pieces of light gauge "hoop iron" (steel band) approximately $\frac{3}{4}$ to 1 in. [19 to 25 mm]. This made a very comfortable home.

'Timber was used for the wallplates. Sometimes they would also put a length of wood in a long wall to act as a binder but this just

2.8 Detail of the above building showing a lath and daub gable above a clay lump wall

weakened the wall and no one could ever tell me why this was continued. Hanging pictures was no problem, they just hammered nails direct into clay lump; all fixtures were likewise. Doors and windows were made in the carpenters' workshops and openings were made as the wall was built.

'Red pammets 9 × 9 in. to 12 × 12 in. [225 × 225 mm to 300 × 300 mm] were laid on a bed of dry ashes or sand for the floor. They never got damp then. This would never be done today. I don't think we have advanced; we have gone backwards.*

'After the clay lump in the wall had been exposed to the weather they would plaster it over with one coat, or perhaps two coats of clay which sometimes contained just a little short straw in it. There was more chalk in the plaster than in the lumps, it could have been marl from the local chalk pits or they might have put lime in it. I don't know.

'You can only plaster with clay on clay; nothing else will do. The same with the interior. Never gypsum or cement; the clay lump will reject it in a short time. The only answer, if replastering was required, was to net the whole area with ¾ or 1 in. [19 or 25 mm] galvanized wire netting and plaster the whole with 2½ lime : 1 sand together with cow hair well raked in.

'There is a high shrinkage in clay. After rendering the first coat, you marked it all over in a diamond pattern with a piece of stick to prepare it for the next coat. It used to go on like creamy butter.

'Most houses are covered with tar and *ruddle* [red ochre] on top of the render. They gave it a first coat of tar and let that dry. They would then give it a second coat of tar and,

* Certainly many of the damp problems associated with old buildings today are due to the insertion of damp-proof membranes and concrete floors. Moisture is unable to evaporate and its only means of escape is usually through the walls.

2.9 Blo Norton, Norfolk. The results of a hard cement-based render on a clay lump wall

2.10 Detail of the barn at Blo Norton

while that was still wet, they would mix a slurry of lime and sand and rub that into the wet tar. You used a 10 oz [283 g] grass brush and the secret was to get the slurry in while the second coat of tar was still wet. It was very hard work because the naptha in the tar was sticky and the sand and the lime was a thick

2.11 Tarred barn at Great Hockham, Norfolk. The tar acted as a deterrent to rats, mice and other vermin

cream. You could almost break the wrist using it. You didn't smooth it; the surface was rough like the face of a brick. You would leave it for three months and the tar would bleed through and it would come out looking like a "golden guinea". Some people would leave it like that but most would give it two coats of colour wash afterwards. After a further couple of months you would cover it with two coats of limewash and it would be all right for 20 to 25 years. No water would get through.

Repairs and reuse of old clay lump

'When I started building in 1928, aged 14, my generation didn't want to know about clay; they wanted modern clean materials. They simply knocked down the old clay lump walls and put bricks in. Also lime was on the way out; they were only interested in cement. *Cement Kings* we called them.

'When we repaired these old buildings we were not allowed to take a piece of clay away; all the old stuff was kept in a heap. You took any stones or old bits of wood out of it; then threw plenty of water on and left it until it was ready to use again. When the old clay had become "dead" we would put a bit of lime on to liven it up. I can't tell you how we knew it was dead; it was only by working with it that

2.12 Detail of a clay lump wall at Saham Toney, Norfolk. The unprotected blocks show signs of merging together

one could tell it was a bit flat. We also put a little sand in to sharpen it up. Chopped straw about 6 in. [150 mm] was puddled in with an old, short, four-tined garden fork. It had a consistency rather like a macaroni pudding.

'During the early to mid twenties my father had the job of adding two wings to an old cottage for the late Breckland novelist, MICHAEL HOME (CHRISTOPHER BUSH). The house still stands at the junction of Walton and Vicarage Roads at Great Hockham. An old workhouse was being pulled down at nearby Rocklands and the lumps were being sold. Mr Home bought a great many of them and loose clay was saved. The clay was broken up with 7 lb [3.17 kg] hammers; it was soaked with water, and plenty of chopped straw was puddled in with a short four-tined fork. It was then put into moulds, sun hardened and transported to Hockham where the new wings were to be built. Stock sizes of lumps, as a rule of thumb guide, were 10 or 8 × 15 × 9 in. or 20 × 12 × 9 in. [250 or 200 × 375 × 225 mm or 500 × 300 × 225 mm]. But of course there were wide variations. I remember spending many hours helping as a boy of about 12 years old; it was hard and dirty work laying lump. Everyone wore a stout sack apron for this job; I well remember my mother making mine out of sugar, flour or railway corn sacks.

'We netted over a house, near the pub in the village, and applied sand and lime mortar. We then threw shingle on and pressed it in with a flat pad made from a piece of wood fixed to the end of a broom stick. We had a pile of shingle and would either throw fistfuls at the wall or just flick it on with a plastering trowel; there was a real art to it.

'Netting is necessary if anything other than clay is used for a render. Roughcast was not suitable because it had cement mixed in with the slurry. In latter years they used to net walls over and render with cement or other modern finishes; but they are so hard-looking and the finish will only last until the net and nails rust through.

'When repairing holes in exterior renders we always used clay. For very small inside repairs we might have used plaster of Paris but this had to be "killed" with human urine so that it did not set too quickly; we also added a little sand. Larger areas were repaired with lime and sand into which was incorporated well beaten cow hair, in the ratio of $2\frac{1}{2}:1$.

'We had one man who used cow dung in plaster for interior and exterior work and inside chimneys. It was important that the dung was fresh and had the morning dew still on it; it would make anything stick. Another builder would use urine in all types of plaster and also in colour wash. I have thought since that this was similar to adding salt. In those days we were not aware of the chemical content of a material; we only knew that an additive was performing a useful purpose. Nowadays we would ask a chemist to analyse the material.

'For limewash, chalk lime was the best. When the local chalk works went out of production we used to buy lime from Derbyshire then slake it. We would throw the water on and make a nice fat putty with it. We added some copperas [ferrous sulphate], some Russian fat (tallow), a little yellow ochre or Venetian red and a shovel or two of sand; sometimes we left it pure white. The Russian fat would keep it waterproof for a couple of years. In later years when we could not get Russian tallow I put linseed oil in or, if they wanted a cheap job done, some paraffin to help keep it waterproof. A little bit of salt, alum, milk, rice water or urine would also make it hard and waterproof.

2.13 A clay lump house at Blo Norton

'Animals will lick clay lump and damage it but cow dung mixed with render will stop it. Chickens will peck a lump wall and an old turkey has been known to pick a lump to pieces to obtain some of the mineral content of the material.'

3 MUD WALLS

Cob

There were local variations in both the consistency of the mud used for building, depending upon the chalk, clay, sand or gravel content of the soil of the area, and the way in which the courses were laid. In some instances straw was laid on top of each course which helped to throw the water away from the wall.

Straw, or some other form of binder, incorporated in the mix made the mud easier to tread and to handle when building. It strengthened the wall and slowed down erosion; it also aided drying, helped combat shrinkage and reduced cracks.

In building a wall one man stood on the ground and threw the mud/straw mix up to a man standing on top of the wall; the second man laid the cob in diagonal layers to each horizontal course and then trod the mix firmly into place. A 'raise' or 'lift' was about 12 in. (300 mm) high but could be less or more. Each lift was allowed to settle for a few days before the next was applied. The wall was then trimmed and pared down using a spade-like tool known as a *paring-iron*.

3.1 A cob building at Bow, Devon

3.2 Detail of the cob building shown in figure 3.1

Lintels for doors and windows were inserted as walls were raised and the openings

3.3 A clay/mud barn at Kirkbride, Cumbria

3.4 Detail of the above barn

3.5 Lamonby Farmhouse, Burgh by Sands, Cumbria. The clay mud walls were repaired and limewashed in 1982 and the roof rethatched

below them were cut out later. Walls were normally 18 to 24 in. (450 to 600 mm) thick: where walls are very thick this may be due to subsequent layers of cob being applied to the exterior surface over many years. When walls were sufficiently dry some were rendered with roughcast or a slurry of cob; many were limewashed and others were left in their natural state.

Failure of these buildings today is often associated with recent alterations. Damp-proof courses inserted in a wall can weaken the structure. A damp-proof membrane inserted under the floor area may drive moisture up the cob walls. Although mud walls are good in compression they have a low tensile strength and alterations to the roof may impair their solidity. New window or door openings, especially near corners of a building, may endanger the wall. Foundations can be undermined by new drains or drainage trenches. Cement renders will trap moisture within a wall. Because of the homogeneous nature of cob the whole wall will sometimes collapse intact.

Devon cob

MR ALFRED HOWARD, a builder and cob consultant at Copplestone, Devon, is now training and advising people how to build and repair these walls using traditional methods.

'Transport was difficult in the past', says MR HOWARD, 'and when they built a house they used whatever material could be found on the site. Once the house was built they started on the farm buildings. There were two purposes in using cob; as they dug the clay out of the ground they made a reservoir for the cattle to drink from; and cob was chosen because it is the warmest material for walls. Cattle do far better in old cob buildings, where the temperature stays on an even keel, than they would in modern sheds. In modern farm buildings cattle will sometimes suffer from double pneu-

3.6 Lamonby Farm

3.7 Detail of the barn at Lamonby Farm, Burgh by Sands, Cumbria

3.8 Devon cob

3.9 Detail of the above cob wall

monia due to the extremes of temperature but they seldom had this in the old buildings.'

Mud buildings throughout the world often contain dung. It has been said that the dung acted as a binder and as an added protection against damp penetration. But ALFRED HOWARD believes that 'the reason cow dung is found in Devon cob is that the best way to mix and prepare the cob, in the past, was to keep two little bullocks in a square pen that had straw in it. The bullocks trod the cob; the more it is trod the better it is; it is like making a cake. One of the reasons why they used small bullocks is that a man's foot isn't really the right shape; a bullock's foot is small and it pushes the straw harder than a foot could do; it goes right into the cob. Even little children may have helped with the treading because you find heels from their shoes where they were pulled off. Old clay pipes are also sometimes found in cob. Treading is still used; nobody has been sufficiently interested to develop a machine.

'You can't make cob without straw. The straw is added, uncut, to the clay. One problem today is that the farmer uses fertilizer on the land to get more grain but this makes the straw weaker; the more fertilizer you use, the weaker the straw. This is why straw must be winter grown which is tougher than spring corn because it has been growing longer and has withstood the winter. Winter corn is tilled in autumn and harvested in September. Spring corn is tilled in spring and harvested in September.

'Rising damp only goes up as far as the stonework of the plinth. When it gets to the cob it stops provided the cob has plenty of clay in it; cob is a natural waterproofer in itself. If damp does rise it will go up by the plaster if there is cement in it. Cement is the biggest detrement to cob that you can get. It is too hard, too brittle and too dense. I saw three cob walls come down one very wet winter and this was because of cement rendering; water had got in through cracks in the render and had become trapped. As it got into the wall it brought the cob out.

'With some walls it is wise to protect the cob but others do not need it. Lime, sand and cows' hair is all that you should use for a render.

'The difference between a new building and an old one is that now they make materials so dense. They have failed to realize that walls must "breathe". This is why there are problems with condensation; before the war this was almost unheard of. It is because moisture in the air condenses against the dense material of the wall, as with glass, whereas years ago it was absorbed into the plaster and it just dried out again.

'Cows' hair was used for internal plaster; they also used horse hair. Years ago one could buy horse hair by the hundredweight; they would buy 6 cwt [46.2 kg] at a time. It had been treated so that one could keep it like lime: you used to beat it with a stick. All the old lath and plaster ceilings had hair in them and this is why they are still there after 300 to 400 years. I have a cottage at Down St Mary where the plaster has hay or grass in it. They also used hay and heather to bind cob.

'Limewash was used for decoration. If they wanted it tinted they used earth colours. For a cream colour they soaked yellow clay in water and poured that into the limewash or whitewash; for pink they used red earth.'

Mr Howard says that central heating does not harm a cob building; he compares the situation with earth structures in African countries that have survived for hundreds of years. He believes that the longevity of African structures may also be partly attributed to building with blocks.

Alfred Howard has made cob blocks which he intends to use for repairing walls; the cob was moulded in wooden boxes and has been allowed to dry throughout the summer.

'To repair cracks in a wall you have to be careful. You can't always repair old cob with new cob. You can put new cob on top of old cob but you cannot fill a crack in an old wall with new cob because the two would not marry together; as new cob dries out it will shrink. Many people have filled cracks using bits of brick but all they are doing is splitting the wall apart instead of repairing it. You must cut out and straighten the crack; then tie in at intervals with tiles. Cob blocks or cob bricks made from old dry cob mixed with lime and straw can be used for wider cracks.

'To rebuild a garden wall we used material that we got from the old wall and we added fresh straw. It is not always necessary to add lime in Devon but in a lime county, such as Dorset, it may be a good thing to mix lime with the cob.

'Thatch on the top of boundary walls was fixed in the same way as for houses. They had wooden wall plates which were fixed with wooden pegs into the cob. Wheat rolls were tied onto the plate with tarred cord and the thatch was sparred into the roll. Where wood was not available for a wall plate on a garden wall they would spar straight into the cob.

'There is more interest today in old buildings, including cob, than ever before. I have people coming to see me from all walks of life and they all want to create something with their own hands, such as, building with cob, wood carving, etc. As with medicine they are going back to some of the old ideas; the old herbs and the foxglove seem to be more effective than some of the modern drugs.

'The problem is not so much building with cob but in keeping the old buildings. Architects and the Building Regulations are sometimes the biggest enemies. Unless people understand what they are doing in repairing and altering an old cob building they are

3.10 Repairs to thatch at Coleford, Devon

going to lose a lot more. There are not enough people with experience of cob to deal with these old buildings. Building with cob is hard work and a messy job and nobody in this day and age wants to do this. Experience is needed in repair work and I am willing to train young people and teach them the knowledge I have gained over the years.'

Mr Howard wishes to stress the point that 'a cob wall is like a baby, it *must* have a dry hat and a dry bottom'.

ACKNOWLEDGMENT

I gratefully acknowledge the help and information provided by the following building craftsmen:

Mr Gowen Ditchburn, Goodworth Clatford, Hampshire
Mr Alfred Howard, Copplestone, Devon
Mr RA Moulding, Great Wishford, Wiltshire

FURTHER READING

See *Select bibliography* under section '*Unbaked Earth Walling*', page 166.

4 CHALK

The nature of chalk

Chalk is one of the purest, whitest and the finest grained of our building limestones. It is not only easy to quarry but is also the most workable of stones and has been widely used for both secular and ecclesiastical buildings; it was the perfect material for finely carved interior work, as can be seen in the Lady Chapel (1321 to 1349) of Ely Cathedral and the many churches where chalk was readily available. The material is in abundant supply but the craftsmen who worked it have disappeared and the use of chalk in building today is confined almost entirely to work in conservation.

The chalklands of England stretch in four main belts radiating from the wide central chalk area of Salisbury Plain; in the north-easterly direction through the Chilterns to Norfolk with a further outcrop from Lincolnshire to the Yorkshire Wolds; eastwards through Surrey to the white cliffs of Dover; south-eastwards through Hampshire to Brighton and south-westwards through Dorset to Beer Head in Devon.

Chalk is a soft limestone. It is composed of about 10 per cent microscopic marine organisms (known as *Foraminifera*) and fragments of other larger shells. In its purest state it may be composed of up to 98 per cent calcium carbonate in the form of mineral calcite.

Chalk building stone is found in three discrete hard bands in the Chalk strata:

1. *Totternhoe Stone* is formed near the base of the Lower Chalk; it appears in the stratum below the Grey Chalk, used for making lime, and above that of the Chalk Marl which is, in part, used for making cement.
2. *Melbourn Rock* is from the basal band of the Middle Chalk and is found below the shelly chalk containing calcite crystals.
3. *Chalk Rock* is from the base of the Upper Chalk; it is beneath the white chalk containing nodular and tabular flints.

Within the Great Chalk Formation variations occur in the texture, strength and colour of the chalk according to the stratum from which it is obtained. Further changes are apparent in different parts of the country; in Lincolnshire and Yorkshire the chalk is predominantly hard whereas in some areas, such as the Isle of Wight, it tends to be too porous for general use as a building stone.

Where chalk stone was not readily available, walls of cottages, farm buildings and boundaries were built of pulverized chalk, mixed with water, to form pugged chalk; or with clay to form chalk-mud.

4.1 The chalk belt of England

Pugged chalk and chalk-mud walling

Unbaked earth has been used from earliest times for building simple structures; the material was cheap, insulation good and condensation rare. Methods of construction varied from place to place according to traditional practice and the nature of the chalk or clay that was readily available.

The three basic types of construction were:

1 *Cob* or the *piled method*
2 *Pisé* or the *shuttered method*
3 *Pugged chalk* or *chalk-mud lump*.

Where soft well-weathered chalk could be found close to the surface, it was pulverized, mixed with water and used in these ways. Chalk was also added to clay to act as a binder and this was known as *chalk-mud walling*. Chalk provided additional strength and durability to a wall; it also gave a quicker set to a mix and helped to overcome part of the inherent weakness of building with mud with its tendency to shrink and crack on drying when newly constructed, or, in an old wall, to swell when subjected to continued dampness and thus become vulnerable to frost damage. Proportions of chalk to clay varied depending upon the area: CF Innocent in his book *The Development of English Building Construction* (page 137) cites 3 parts chalk to 1 part clay in Hampshire.

4.2 A dovecote at Toft, Cambridgeshire. The nesting boxes are of pre-cast pugged chalk blocks. Photograph by courtesy of John McCann

Around the Aylesbury area of Buckinghamshire there is a belt that consists of a natural blend of clay and chalk; this material was known as *wychert*, *witchert* or *white earth*, and when mixed with straw and water formed an ideal chalk conglomerate material for building. The wychert of Haddenham was found close to the surface and was considered the best; the piled method of construction was used and many cottages and boundary walls of this material remain at Haddenham, Long Credon, Aylesbury and the surrounding countryside.

In some areas, notably Wiltshire and Cambridgeshire, pugged chalk or chalk-mud lump was set into moulds to form blocks of approximately twice the size of a modern brick. A dryish mix, similar to that used in pisé work, was compressed by treading and smoothing with a spade into a pre-wetted rectangular mould without base or top; the mould was removed and the blocks left to dry in the sun for a few weeks. The blocks were set in lime mortar or puddled clay in courses; walls of chalk lump are often difficult to distinguish from those built of chalk rock.

The pisé method required a dryish mix; the moisture content was important; if too wet the pugged chalk shrank upon drying, if too dry it failed to consolidate on ramming. The pugged chalk was placed between movable horizontal boards that formed a trough; the shuttering was supported on the outside by posts and held together internally with cross pieces. The mix was compressed with a rammer.

Chalk was best weathered by exposure to frost before use; where newly dug the chalk was difficult to grind and if small nodules of chalk remained in a mix they tended to absorb damp and 'explode' when the wall was subjected to frost.[1] Building took place from spring to autumn and was completed before the onset of frost.

It was essential in building with this material that each rise, or course, was sufficiently dry before the next was laid. The wall was covered at night as a protection against rain.

Chalk conglomerate walls required a good 'hat' or overhang at eaves level for their survival; these walls are good in compression but have no great lateral strength; the roofs

4·3 Chalk conglomerate cottage at Broad Chalke, Wiltshire

4·4 Chalk conglomerate wall disintegrating through damp and frost action. Upavon, Wiltshire

4.5 Traditional thatch coping to chalk cob wall near Martin, Hampshire

4.6 Loss of render to chalk conglomerate wall. Upavon, Wiltshire

were tied and had a light covering material but the traditional thatch has been largely replaced by tiles today.

Protection was needed from rising damp. A brick or stone plinth known as the *underpin course*[2] was built 18 to 24 in. (450 to 600 mm) or more above ground level to form a butt against rainwater splashback. The underpin course was sometimes tarred as a further protection and broken glass was occasionally added as a deterrent from vermin attack.

ROBERT MENNELL, writing about the building of his chalk house in 1920, said the view of the Ministry of Agriculture at that time was that 'provided the chalk cob walls rest on virgin chalk, they may be safely erected without brick or concrete foundations'. Mr MENNELL, nevertheless, in his own building work, took no chances and incorporated a damp-proof course above concrete foundations.[3]

Fireplaces, flues and chimneys were usually of brick or stone. Where chimneys were built of pugged-chalk they were durable but are said to have required more frequent sweeping. Door and window frames were fixed to large pieces of timber set across the thickness of the wall. Lintels were of wood; and oak posts were placed in position in the reverse to their way of growth. Timbers in contact with chalk conglomerate materials have survived remarkably well.

The permeability of pugged-chalk walls is generally low and many have survived without a protective render. In some areas they were coated with a two-coat lime-hair render or with 'slap-dash'. Walls were allowed to dry out for a year before the render was applied. Limewash, with tallow or linseed oil incorporated, provided a further barrier against damp penetration.

REFERENCES

1 CLIFTON-TAYLOR, ALEC, *The Pattern of English Building*, Faber, 1972.

2 WILLIAMS ELLIS, C, *Cottage Building in Cob, Pisé, Chalk and Clay*, *Country Life*, 1919.

3 MENNELL, ROBERT O, *Building in Chalk*, *Country Life*, September 10, 1943.

ACKNOWLEDGMENT

I gratefully acknowledge the information and help provided by:

Ms Jessica Albery
Mr Gordon Pearson
Mr R A Moulding
Mr Gowen Ditchburn
Mr Martyn Owen
Mr Jack Nelms
Mr Roger Evans

The illustration of the dovecote at Toft, Cambridgeshire is reproduced by courtesy of Mr John McCann.

5 WYCHERT (chalk-cob)

MR JACK NELMS, a recently retired builder and the owner of a long established family firm of builders at Haddenham, Buckinghamshire, spoke of his experience of building with wychert. He is one of the last craftsmen to have built and repaired walls in this material and his information is drawn from his practical building experience following the traditional methods as used by his father-in-law and grandfather-in-law of the Webb family.

5.2

5.1 and 5.2 A wychert house and outbuildings at Haddenham, Buckinghamshire

He has lived most of his life in a fine old wychert house which he describes as warm in winter, cool in summer and free from condensation; he says that he would not live in a house built of a material other than wychert.

The majority of old houses and many of the boundary walls at Church End, Haddenham, are built of wychert. The wychert here was considered the best in the locality and indents in the landscape can be seen in many places from where the material was dug. The limestone rubble used for the base of the walls was also quarried locally and easily at a depth of about 39 in. (1 m) below the surface. The last house to be built in the area is thought to be at Scotsgrove in 1929. Attempts were made in the 1950s and '60s to revive the craft but building labourers were reluctant to work with the material; work has therefore been restricted mainly to repair.

By the 1930s wychert was no longer dug from the ground, and reconstituted wychert from old walls was used. As a wall was demolished lumps of the material were stored in a pit until needed. Preparation for work using salvaged material was similar to that using it newly dug. It was broken down with a spade and fork and by treading; any large stones were removed.

When required for use the wychert was removed to the building site and spread on the ground along the length of the wall. Water was added and it was strewn with straw. The addition of straw helped to form a cohesive mix with a consistency suitable for lifting with a fork. JACK NELMS described the process: 'You held a bundle of wheat straw under the arm and scattered it, uncut, onto the wychert. Then, wearing heavy boots (Wellington boots were not suitable) you trod it in well. It was a heavy job as feet became stuck in the putty-like mix; it was best trod by carthorses and turned by men.

'Two special wychert forks were used, and these, with a spade and plumb-bob, were the only tools needed; the forks were long handled and had small heads consisting of three steel prongs. Building commenced in April, continued throughout summer and, when weather permitted, into the autumn. Protection was needed against rain, and work ceased before danger of frost.

'A stone rubble base known as the *grumping* prevented contact between the wychert and ground. The grumping was without footings; it was taken down to a solid base of between 12 and 36 in. [300 and 900 mm] below ground level and rose 24 to 36 in. [600 to 900 mm] above the adjoining ground. The thickness of the wychert wall ranged from 16 to 24 in. [400 to 600 mm] with 16 in. [400 mm] being the most common. During building an extra 2 to 3 in. [50 to 75 mm] or more was added to either side of the wall which was pared back later.'

Building was a two-man operation with both labourer and craftsman using a wychert fork. MR NELMS gives the following description of the process. 'The labourer stood on the ground digging with one of the forks and I would be on top of the wall: I would hold my fork down and the man would dig a spit full; he would then "clop" it, we call "clock" it, over onto my fork. I picked my fork up and I would "clock" it, "clack" it (perhaps from the Flemish *klacken*: to remove dirty clots, etc) onto the wall. Normally you built your wall much wider than 16 or 18 in. [400 or 450 mm] and with the straw hanging down. When it had dried you would trim it using an ordinary spade held on its side (not the part used for digging). Then using a plumb-bob, to get your upright, you would cut into the wall with a chisel every 48 or 60 in. [1220 or 1524 mm] or so, and complete the trimming back.

'The wall was built in "burys" [rises]; they were always 24 to 30 in. [600 to 760 mm] high and never more than 36 in. [900 mm]. If you exceeded that height in one block, and when the next bury was added, the lower bury wouldn't dry properly and would "spew out". If you tried to rush it and get on top of it, then the weight of it would cause it to "go out", to bulge. Once it started to move before it was dry it would keep on going for perhaps two hours; there was nothing one could do to stop it. It was no good propping it up. It was not possible to pare it back later; the section of the wall had to be rebuilt.'

The time taken for each bury to dry depended upon the weather; in summer this might be a week. In building a house it was often possible to continue work without interruption if it took a week to work round the perimeter of the building.

Wychert varied, explained Mr NELMS. 'In some places it was not as good as others. Haddenham wychert was good; working on them all, as we did, you could always tell where it had come from when you put a new opening into a wall; one could recognize it by the way it chiselled out; it might be hard, as it should be, or crumble easily. Wychert is easy stuff to work with; with good wychert you can cut into a wall for a window or door opening provided it is done with care. It does not crumble and you can saw it as cleanly as if it were wood.'

5·3 Wychert cottages and garden walls at Haddenham, Buckinghamshire

For inserting a new window two oak lintels were used. The interior face of the wall would be cut out first and the lintel placed in position; this would be repeated on the exterior. 'Provided the timbers were suitable there was no limit to the size of the opening.'

Rebuilding a section of collapsed wychert wall, including the corners, using wychert does not appear to have the problems of bonding associated with the mud–cob wall of the West Country where brick or stone is often considered necessary. Reconstituted wychert may be applied to a wetted surface. The work, however, is labour intensive and today, unfortunately, repairs are done using concrete blocks which are then rendered over.

Wychert, unrendered, is a soft, pale golden-yellow colour with a pleasing texture. Many of the old houses and boundary walls at Church End, Haddenham, are rendered. But, adds Mr NELMS, 'it is not necessary to render provided you have a "good hat" on it, that is the capping, to protect it; both houses and boundary walls were originally thatched with straw but now local tiles are used. You can spray water onto a wall and the wychert will absorb it, but it will not stand running water, such as a leaking gutter. Wychert was never intended to be rendered. They rendered boundary walls on the road side, to look tidier I suppose, but not on the field side, and it spoils it. I would like to see the render off. I like to see the real stuff; just as my father-in-law and his father before him did.

'These walls can be expensive to repair if not well maintained. The stone grumpings are to keep the wychert off the wet ground but people do not understand this and will tip garden rubbish against a wall; when wychert gets wet, the frost will fetch it down.

'Lime is the only material you can use with wychert. It hates the smell of cement or gypsum. When replastering an old wall you take off the old plaster; and whether it is 200 years old or new, you always wet the wychert.

5.4 A rendered wychert wall that has been repeatedly patched. The wall would originally have had a thatched coping with a good overhang to protect the wall. There would have been no need for a render

You have a bucket set aside, and work on roughly a square yard [square metre] at a time. If you tap with your hand on the walls of every house in the village you get a hollow sound; this is because the suction of the wychert is so great, and by wetting the surface the suction is held back a little. The mortar goes off so quickly there is no need to use cement. You use a weak mix of pure lime mortar; 6 or 7 buckets of sand to one of lime. Two coats are used and if you want to add a little cement in the second coat this would be all right. A rough finish to match the wychert is best.'

Many of the older houses in the village have flues constructed with wychert and these have continued in use for more than 200 years without problems.

6 PRE-CAST PUGGED CHALK BLOCKS

6.1 and **6.2** Houses at Quarley, Hampshire, built of pre-cast pugged chalk blocks

Hugh's Settlement was founded after the First World War. Initially a pair of bungalows had been built but the project had been interrupted due to lack of funds. In 1932 it was decided to build a group of cottages at Quarley in Hampshire; these were to be designed in the vernacular style using local materials. Economy, in both cost and time, was of prime importance; unskilled labour was readily available and chalk was the chosen material.

JESSICA ALBERY, a young architect, was invited to design and supervise the buildings. Chalk, if provided with an adequate damp-proof course, would ensure that the houses would be free from damp and condensation; thermal and sound insulation would be good, and local experience had proved that chalk fared well in the event of fire. A large Victorian house in the Quarley area that was built of brick and chalk had suffered a serious fire; as a result the brick became cracked and crumbled but the chalk, although discoloured pink, had withstood the fire. However, the standing chalk walls that no longer had the protective roof, and when later subjected to rain, gradually disintegrated.

The first house, called 'Albery' after the architect, was commenced in 1932, and like those constructed subsequently, was built into the side of a chalk hill. As the chalk for the

6.2

walls was hacked out of the hillside a level platform was provided for the site of the house. The chalk was used as it was dug; it was not broken up by weathering throughout the winter months, as had been done traditionally for pugged chalk, but was pulverized by passing it through a small circular pan-mixer. Building commenced in March when all danger of frost had passed.

JESSICA ALBERY specified a non-porous foundation that was to be taken up to 12 to 18 in. (300 to 450 mm) above the surrounding ground level. She noted that 'chalk will cling to itself but when dry shows a marked antipathy to cling to anything else. Thus most chalk houses rest upon their foundations without actually being attached to them. If it is considered necessary to key the walls into their foundations, this can be done by "cupping" the foundations to a depth of 2 to 3 in. [50 to 76 mm] along their horizontal surfaces to a width of 6 to 8 in. [150 to 200 mm]. The damp-proof course, in the form of a bitumastic strip lying on the foundations, will be depressed by the weight of the wall into the cupping.'

For the first house it was decided to use the *shuttering method* of construction. Resin-bonded plywood sheets approximately 8 ft (2.438 m) high bolted together in the manner of flanged plates formed the shutters. A pugged chalk and hair mix was poured into the moulds. The chalk, however, failed to dry and when, after a few weeks, the shuttering was removed, shrinkage cracks appeared. It was thought that this might have been due to the shutters being of too great a depth. The

6.3 Chalk lumps
1 Scaffolding board
2 chalk lump
3 bricks

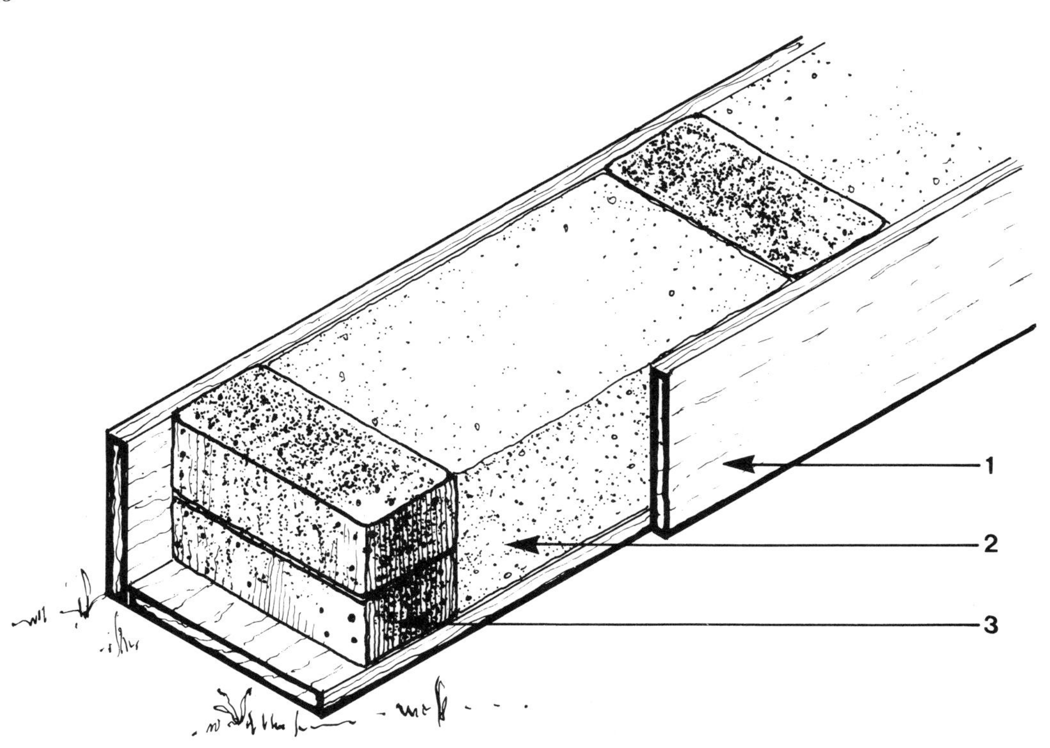

method was considered unsuitable and the alternative, *piled cob*, way of building too slow. An experiment was therefore planned using the pre-cast pugged chalk system and this proved to be very successful. The pugged chalk and straw mix was formed into rough blocks and built in the manner of stone ashlar.

Exterior walls were 18 in. (450 mm) thick without a cavity. Moulds for the blocks were made using three 6 in. (150 mm) scaffolding planks placed on the ground, one flat and the others upright to form a long narrow trough. Bricks were placed transversely across the trough with their distances apart carefully measured. The dimensions of the finished blocks were 18 × 9 × 6 in. (450 × 230 × 150 mm). The outer boards were removed after a day to hasten drying and the blocks were ready for use in building within a further day or two depending upon the weather.

Chalk blocks also proved structurally sound for the 6 in. (150 mm) internal, and 4 in. (100 mm) partition walls; the material provided particularly good sound insulation between rooms. A small block-making machine, with a lever to eject the blocks, was used for the 4 in. (100 mm) walls; these blocks were 4 × 9 × 12 in. (100 × 230 × 300 mm).

The 23 ft (7 m) wide gable walls were built to a height of 20 ft (6 m); the main 53 ft (16 m) long walls were built one and a half storeys high with dormer windows to the bedrooms. These walls are fine in compression but have no strength in tension; the roof must be tied and have a light covering which, in this case, was thatch. Openings were formed as the wall was constructed using 14 × 7½ in. (355 × 200 mm) oak lintels internally and concrete lintels reinforced with old iron pipes for the external walls. If further doors or windows were thought desirable there would have been no problem cutting openings in the completed walls.

Chimneys were constructed of chalk and taken up to the full height above the thatched roof. Ordinary drain pipes were used to line the chimneys. Fireplaces were lined with bricks.

Bedding mortar was made up of pugged chalk and sand. It was important that the mortar should be no stronger than the pugged chalk blocks; therefore no lime was incorporated.

A lime/hair plaster was used internally and a lime plaster without hair externally. The mix was 1 cement : 2 lime : 10 sand. The render was protected with a coloured limewash which included linseed oil; tallow instead of linseed oil would have been equally suitable. The blocks, with their rough uneven texture, provided a good key for the render.

This house was, as Miss ALBERY says, 'built on a shoestring and was a delight to live in'. The cost of building was 8d a cubic foot, labour £28.14.3, and building materials £7.4.5.

7 CLUNCH

Clunch is defined in the *Shorter Oxford English Dictionary* as 'a soft limestone forming one of the beds of the Lower Chalk . . . and any of the various stiff clays. 1679'. The word may be derived from the Dutch *Klontje*: a lump or clod of earth. The term was originally used by builders and miners for any hard and stiff clay; it is still used in Bedfordshire and Cambridgeshire to describe the local chalk-stone but is not applied to similar stone outside this area. It is not a word recognized by geologists.

7.2

7.1 and **7.2** The clunch quarry at Totternhoe

DONOVAN PURCELL in his book *Cambridge Stone* points out that in the fifteenth and sixteenth centuries 'clunch' meant specifically stone from the Burwell rock bed, and 'whyte stone' referred to the softer chalk which was used for internal work and the cores of walls.

Clunch is harder, and more dense and gritty in texture than pure chalk; this is because of the minute fragments of shell and sand in its composition. It is mid-grey in the quarry but weathers to a pale creamy grey with a slight greenish tint; it is similar to Caen stone in appearance but Caen is greener in colour. The surface of clunch can be easily scratched with the finger-nail which distinguishes it from other stones.

Clunch is light in weight and easy to carve. It was the ideal material for internal work and was widely used for vaulting, mouldings and decorative work as can be seen in the Lady Chapel of Ely Cathedral, the Saxon rood at Walkern Church, the fourteenth-century carved images in St Stephen's Chapel, Westminster, the organ screen at Peterborough Cathedral and the many church interiors in Bedfordshire and Hertfordshire. It was relatively durable for plain external walls; notable examples are at Woburn Abbey, Ashridge House, Hitchin Priory and the many churches in the clunch belt. Mr PETER HANDY, a builder at Puckeridge, Hertfordshire, says 'Wrongly laid clunch will disintegrate within ten years but good quality clunch, correctly laid, will last three or four centuries'.[1]

The best known clunch came from Bedfordshire where it was known as *Totternhoe Stone* and from Cambridgeshire where the same stone was known as *Burwell Rock*. Similar stone was obtained from the outcrop that extended from Bedfordshire through Hertfordshire to Cambridgeshire where the bed attained its maximum thickness. Old quarries included those at Cherry Hinton, Reach, Isleham, Barrington, Eversden and Haslingfield; Arlesey closed at the beginning of this century and Burwell in 1960. The last pit at Totternhoe was closed in 1914 but was reopened by H G Clarke and Son in 1982; the Totternhoe Lime and Stone Company is the only organization producing clunch today.

Totternhoe, otherwise known as *Tothenhoe*, *Totornho* or *Totenehou* (*Domesday Book*), is sometimes referred to in medieval documents, in relation to its stone, as *Egremont*, *Eglemunt* or *Eglemont*;[2] these names appear to have reverted to the older name Totternhoe from the fifteenth century.

Totternhoe clunch is now worked from an open quarry but in the past was worked from a network of caves. PETER KALM, a Swede, visited the quarry in 1748 and gave the following account of the caves:[3]

> 'On both sides of the main adit there went other adits, both at acute, right and obtuse angles; so that if the entrances of all these cross-galleries had been open there would have been, to one unacquainted with them, the worst labyrinth and maze there could possibly be; but these adits were now mostly filled up with the loose bits of freestone which had been broken off in the process of hewing.
>
> 'We also noticed the occurrence of nodules of pyrites (Crow's gold) and of shells in the stone, and that it was used not only as a building stone, but also for window-frames and door-posts, and arches over fire-places, windows, and doors for several kinds of pedestals and pillars, the bottoms of baking ovens, etc.'

The caves are said to stretch from Totternhoe to Dunstable and the stone was removed from the caves using ash poles as rollers.[4] The clunch when worked with iron tools had an unpleasant odour and the men grew thyme and mint to disguise the smell.[5] When mining ceased some of the caves were used for forcing rhubarb.[6]

A 30 ft (9.144 m) deep quarry is now being worked at Totternhoe. The middle bed is too soft for exterior use. The best clunch, which is used for ashlar, is obtained from the lower beds; vertical fissures within the bed divide the stone into natural slabs weighing up to 60 tons (60.96 tonnes). Stone is being worked from the pillars separating the old caves. At the base of the lower bed, immediately above the Chalk Marl, there is a 7 ft (2.133 m) deep layer of hard clunch that forms a durable building material in exposed positions; this has been used at Hitchin Priory. It is known as *Clunch-Fleck* because it contains pyrites which are discernible as black specks. This bed of Clunch-Fleck was largely unworked as it was originally below the water table.[7]

In the mid-eighteenth century the only tools used were specially sharpened pick axes and ordinary iron wedges and mallets.[8] Today tungsten carbide chain-saws are used to cut the clunch into manageable blocks of 2 to 3 tons (2.03 to 3.04 tonnes); these are lifted from the pit with a 35 ton (35.56 tonnes) crane.

The demand for clunch nowadays is for conservation work or extensions, such as that to the Swan Hotel at Bedford. The softer stone is supplied to schools for carving. Farmers also require 'yard bottom chalk' as a ground covering for farm buildings; this traditional method is said to keep floors of pig sties reasonably dry and is preferred to concrete which is cold for the animals; 3 in. (75 mm) chalk dust is laid 3 to 4 in. (75 to 100 mm) thick on the ground and rammed down hard.

It is interesting to note the use of chalk for threshing floors laid across the widths of old barns; 'the oldest and most enduring material is clunch or rammed chalk which is unique in its ability to resist discolouration, remaining clinically white and clean irrespective of age and wear'.[9]

REFERENCES AND ACKNOWLEDGMENT

1 ROBERTS, EILEEN, *Totternhoe Stone and Flint in Hertfordshire Churches*, Mediaeval Archaeology 1974.
2 SALZMAN, L F, *Building in England down to 1540*, Oxford University Press 1967
3 KALM, PETER, KALM's Account of his visit to England on his way to America in 1748. Translation J LUCAS, London 1892
4 Mr STAN CLARKE, *The Totternhoe Lime and Stone Quarry*
5 Mr STAN CLARKE
6 Mr BRUCE ROBERTS, Manager of the Totternhoe Lime and Stone Quarry
7 Mr STAN CLARKE
8 PETER KALM
9 Essex Countryside Historic Barns, Essex County Council.

USEFUL ADDRESS

Totternhoe Lime and Stone Co Ltd
Lower End, Totternhoe, Dunstable, Bedfordshire.

Clunch in building

Woburn Abbey, Bedfordshire

The Abbey and outbuildings were largely rebuilt and extended by HENRY FLITCROFT in 1747. An extensive programme of repair to the clunch walls of Stable Court and the Abbey has been in progress for several years.

CECIL RHODES, Clerk of Works to the repair work, advocates the use of Totternhoe Clunch but he points out that 'it is a soft stone and therefore requires sensitive handling and a good mason to use it. If carefully maintained it should last several hundred years – even without a damp-proof course.'

TONY HOOD, Master Mason at Woburn, says: 'Clunch is cut into 2-ton blocks at the quarry then delivered to Woburn to "cure" for a minimum of one year, but ideally for two or three years. It is placed under cover in a barn where plenty of air is allowed to circulate. The stone is stacked in the same way as for seasoning wood with strips of timber between each block. Well weathered clunch will "ring" when tapped.'

It is particularly difficult to recognize the natural bed of Totternhoe Clunch so blocks have to be marked at the quarry. Like all sedimentary stone the clunch should be 'natural bedded' in a normal wall; that is, laid with the laminations horizontal as in the quarry.

7.3 The junction between a clunch wall and a plinth constructed of a harder stone poses a problem. Moisture becomes trapped and is absorbed by the clunch which can lead to erosion. Woburn Abbey

7.4 New clunch blocks in the process of being bonded to the rubble backing at Stable Court, Woburn Abbey

Where clunch is wrongly bedded exfoliation can occur within ten years. (CR)

Tony Hood stresses the importance of repairing clunch with clunch. The pore structure of chalk is such that excessive suction causes it to weather and dry differently from other stone; where placed next to hard stone it may fail to dry out properly. The base of a clunch wall will often lead to problems where it is in contact with another stone, such as the Portland stone plinth to the walls at Woburn; moisture becomes trapped above the harder stone and the clunch becomes vulnerable to frost action. Consideration should be given to inserting a damp course to isolate the stones. (TH)

The choice between large-scale renewal, where the stone is partially decayed, or by patching and dressing back is not always easy; the retention of original craftsmanship is important; however, the cost of scaffolding is a significant factor and erosion at a high level may suggest a case for renewal. Figure 7.4 shows new blocks being bonded to the rubble backing at Stable Court. Once in position the new clunch is dressed back to a smooth surface. A 'drag', in the form of a thin plate of steel indented on the edge, is used to scale and rub the soft stone; sanders are also used. (TH)

An early repair method is shown in figure 7.5; individual defective blocks have been dressed back and although care was taken to avoid a ridge at the base of each stone water has settled in some instances. Original stone has been retained but the effect is patchy. The procedure now is to dress back areas of wall

7·5 An early repair method. Badly decayed blocks have been replaced and the old stonework retained where possible and dressed back. Woburn Abbey

where the decay is uniform or to replace single blocks with new. (CR)

Leaking rainwater pipes, and the resulting frost damage, caused spalling on a section of the Abbey wall so ¾ in. (20 mm) has been worked off the face of the old stone which has been redressed to a smooth finish by sanding; air tools have proved successful in producing an even surface. The stone is generally good behind the spalled exterior but where decay is deeper than ¾ in. (20 mm) individual blocks are cut out and replaced. (CR)

Where erosion has been caused by rusted iron cramps small sections of stone are renewed by 'piecing in' new clunch with a minimum 4 in. (100 mm) thickness. Piecing in is only acceptable aesthetically if the decay is not extensive as it spoils the character of the wall. Defective iron cramps have been replaced with stainless steel fixings. (TH)

The ashlar joints are fine and flush. The mortar for bedding and pointing is composed of lime putty, crushed stone and a trace of cement. (TH). Both horizontal and vertical joints are grouted with the aid of V-shaped 'joggles', or grooves; these help to overcome the inherent problem of using an absorbent stone and fine joints; a combination which tends to 'take the nature out of the mortar'. (CR)

Tony Hood says that boiled linseed oil was used on the original masonry of the Abbey. He believes it was a traditional practice to coat all sides of a block of clunch before placing it in the wall; this helped to counter the porosity of the stone when it came into contact with the mortar.

Iron stains, caused by metal windows or tools that have discoloured the clunch, are removed by another traditional method used by masons; the stains are coated with a hot lime poultice; this is allowed to dry then brushed down hard with a stiff brush. (CR)

Fine sculptured work in clunch has been sensitively repaired by Mr Hood. The new and old stone has been rubbed together to provide barely visible joints.

Tony Hood and Cecil Rhodes have different views on conserving the external face of a clunch wall. Cecil Rhodes supports the limewater technique as advocated by Professor Baker at Wells Cathedral; he believes that the limewater restores some of the natural 'sap' that dries out when the stone is cured. On a test area at Woburn they used three coats of limewater to be repeated at five-year intervals. A 12 ft (3.657 m) lance and the use of a ladder was sufficient to treat the walls. But for a higher building, where scaffolding is required, it would be more economical to apply 40 coats of limewater with longer periods between applications.

TONY HOOD considers the medieval practice of using boiled linseed oil is effective. It is important that the oil is *boiled*; when it is applied to the wall it turns the clunch to a greyish tint but the colour returns to normal after a short period. Renewal is necessary about every ten years. CECIL RHODES agrees that boiled linseed oil has an important role to play in certain areas; three-coat applications, to small areas subject to heavy weathering or where water is likely to settle, have proved successful at Woburn.

Mr RHODES and Mr HOOD have both commented on the use of limewash as a protective coating; they say that it is useful on most limestone walls but that it would spoil the beauty of Totternhoe clunch. It has therefore not been applied to the walls at Woburn.

The Research and Technical Advisory Service of the Historic Buildings and Monuments Commission (HBMC) are conducting a series of tests on the west elevation of the south stable block of Woburn Abbey to compare methods of consolidating the clunch. The treatments applied to test panels were 'Brethane alkoxy silane consolidant: Microcrystalline wax: Boiled linseed oil: Lime poultice, limewater and lime-casein shelter coat'. Details are published in *Practical Building Conservation, Stone Masonry, English Heritage Technical Handbook*, Volume 1, by John and Nicola Ashurst, published by the Gower Technical Press 1988.

8 BEER STONE

Beer Stone, from the Middle Chalk, is obtained from a bed in the Beer locality of Devon and is not found elsewhere in the country. For centuries the stone was extracted from the large quarry and underground caverns about one mile west of the village of Beer; it was also quarried a few miles (kilometres) away at Sutton and Hooken Cliff. It has been widely used since Roman times when it was mined, rather than quarried, from the cliff-sides. The Beer quarry is the only one being worked today. It is open to the public during the summer months.

Beer Stone is a moderately coarse-grained cretaceous chalk-stone composed almost entirely of pulverized fragments of inoceramus shells. It is light cream in colour and similar to, but harder and more granular in texture, than Totternhoe clunch. AJ Jukes-Browne[1] describes it as 'stronger than Bath Stone and much superior to Caen Stone which was once so much used in England'. It is soft when fresh but hardens when seasoned by exposure. The stratum of stone at the quarry is of great thickness and free from fissures; blocks of up to eight tons (8.12 tonnes) have been quarried.[2]

PE Masey[3] writing in 1882 noted that: 'The stone has these special advantages – agreeable appearance, fine grain, especially fitting it for delicate carving, and easiness and cheapness of working. It is beyond rivalry the cheapest stone in the market. Its durability for interior work is undoubted, and for exterior purposes it is at least better than many, and I think, equal to any.

'The stone was used extensively for all types of buildings in Devon, Somerset, Dorset and Hampshire; it was used in the fourteenth-century work by William Wykeham at Winchester Cathedral, the crypt of St Stephen's Chapel at Westminster, Rochester Castle, Kent and Exeter Cathedral. Churches include: Charmouth, Lyme Regis, Uplyme, Chard, Colyton, Axminster, Axmouth, Seaton, Branscombe, Ottery St Mary, Honiton, St Lawrence Clist, Whimple and Tallaton.'

Beer Stone in building

Exeter Cathedral

Peter Dare, Master Mason of the Cathedral, says that the durability of Beer Stone varies; he believes that 'stone is best where used close to where it was quarried. A block of stone in a quarry may appear ideal for a piece of work but when removed to another area, perhaps only 20 miles [32.18 km] away, could weather differently and the colour can change. At Broadhembury, which is on high ground between Honiton and Exeter, the Beer Stone grows a red lichen and where red lichen grows this stone weathers best. Ketton Stone from Northamptonshire appeared suitable for Exeter Cathedral but changed colour to a yellow, almost orange, colour when transferred to the site; removal from the dry

8.1 Cottage at Beer, Devon. The Beer Stone window surround 26 years after construction

Northamptonshire air to the damp weather conditions, and perhaps salt in the air, of the West Country changed the quality of the stone'.

PETER DARE cites the case of a cottage built close to the quarry at Beer. He renewed the window surrounds in 1958 using Beer Stone; after 26 years the stone is in the same pristine condition, including the colour as when built. (See figure 8.1)

'Beer Stone fresh from the quarry is soft; it is allowed to season by exposure for a year or two. A slab of, say, 8 ft long × 36 in. thick (2.438 × 914 mm) "green" stone with sap in it will bend perhaps 2 to 3 in. (50 to 75 mm) out of true. The slabs are laid on sleepers and any twists or curves are corrected with wedges.'

As moisture evaporates some of the cementitious matter within the stone is drawn to the surface 'which forms a "callus" approximately $\frac{1}{16}$ in. (2 mm) thick; this hardening of the surface appears after a few weeks'. PETER DARE believes that 'the callus hastens deterioration rather than providing protection to the stone. When damp penetrates a masonry wall salts move and are drawn out with the moisture through the soft beds; this causes exfoliation of the surface of the stone and the cycle of decay is repeated. It is therefore necessary to protect the stone with a soft "shelter coat" which will prevent a callus forming but will, at the same time, allow the salts to be drawn to the surface. The question arises as to whether we should be thinking of protecting the stone with a shelter coat while it is still in the yard'.

The shelter-coat can be prepared using a mix of putty lime and stone-dust; or lime and tallow; or lime and skimmed milk. The surface of the stone is wetted before application. The choice of stone-dust is dictated by the colour required; Salcombe Regis stone-dust is currently used on the Cathedral. PETER DARE finds the slightly stronger lime from Derbyshire is more suitable than Beer lime for this purpose. The addition of skimmed milk strengthens the shelter coat; this is added to the mix in the proportion of 4 skimmed milk: 1 putty lime and stone-dust. A stronger mix of 10 skimmed milk: 1 putty lime and stone-dust has been used over a small area at the top of the 140 ft (42.672 m) high tower. The mix should be strong enough not to wash off but soft enough to prevent a callus forming. The order of mixing is important; the lime and stone-dust are mixed to a putty consistency and the skimmed milk and water are added last.

A shelter coat of this type is estimated to last ten years. Before renewal the surface is washed down; accumulated dirt is softened with mist sprays and washing is completed with a water jet. The lichen at Exeter is light grey in colour and is welcomed as it contributes to the weathering qualities of the stone.

Linseed oil has been used on a small test area at the Cathedral and found not to be suitable as a protective coating to Beer stone; after two years the surface of the stone exfoliated in the same way a callus would behave.

Linseed oil is referred to in the medieval records of Exeter Cathedral in connection with mortar. PETER DARE finds that 'the addition of linseed oil to the mortar will reduce the suction of a porous stone and provide more working time before the mortar "goes off". The mix used at the Cathedral is 14 sand:4 putty lime:½ cement. A cupful of boiled linseed oil is added and beaten up in a bucket of water which is then used to mix the mortar. Care is taken to match original mortar in both colour and texture; a suitable sand is found about ten miles [16.09 km] from Exeter. Hydraulic lime is no longer used because of the uncertainty of the strength'.

REFERENCES

[1] JUKES-BROWNE, AJ, *Memoirs of the Geological Survey of the UK. The Upper Chalk of England*, volume 10.

[2] SMEATON'S *History of the Eddystone Lighthouse.*

[3] MASEY, PE, architect, *Observations on Beer Stone.*

9 ORDINARY CHALK

9.1 The Old School House 1617, Uffington, Oxfordshire. Chalk blocks on a stone base

9.2 Chalk-stone arch to doorway. The Old School House, Uffington

Churches and manor houses as well as numerous cottages were built using ordinary chalk that was neither Totternhoe clunch nor Beer Stone.

The best ordinary chalk for building was that without flints such as:

(a) *Chalk Rock* from the base of the Upper Chalk formation; this contains glauconite grains and phosphatic nodules.

(b) *Melbourn Rock* from the base of the Middle Chalk which contains fossils including brachiopods. This chalk stone was used for interiors, backings to stone walls and rubble cores. At Medmenham in Buckinghamshire, chalk from the upper beds of the Middle Chalk was used for external walls to the church and many of the cottages and houses in the village.

(c) *Grey Chalk* from the bed above Totternhoe Stone in the Lower Chalk formation contains fossils, such as ammonites; the fossils are occasionally seen built into walls. (See figure 9.3.)

The upper beds contain the purest and also the most porous chalk; yet despite porosity permeability is low. Chalk from beds in

9·3 Ammonites in a cottage wall at Kingston Lisle, Oxfordshire

9·4 Split flints and chalk in the wall of St Peter's Church, Medmenham, Buckinghamshire

northern England, Scotland and Ireland contains more cementitious matter, and it is generally harder, than that in the southern areas of England. There is also a hard and compact bed along the western regions of Berkshire and Norfolk.

Ordinary chalk was used for both fine ashlared work and undressed random-rubble walling. There are many examples of walls displaying chalk-stone in combination with stronger materials, such as limestone, brick or flint, forming pleasing patterns in chequers and bands; at Hunstanton in Yorkshire red chalk mixed with white chalk adorns walls of houses. Flint is the natural counterpart to chalk and the two perhaps form the best combination; many a chalk wall is cased externally with flint.

Chalk was widely used in churches for both interior and exterior work; examples include Compton Beauchamp, Oxfordshire, Bicknor in Kent and Boxgrove Priory; the interior of the mainly Norman church at Compton in Surrey is particularly fine. These were built at a time when men used materials that they considered the best available.

Chalk buildings had a good overhang at eaves level and most had a base of tough limestone. Some medieval stone walls had chalk bases and foundations such as those at Kingston upon Hull and the Round Tower of Winchester Castle. Chalk with its absorbent nature provided good acoustic qualities for partitions. Rubble chalk cores to stone walls absorbed the damp; it was also used for this reason behind flint flushwork. Chalk blocks built honeycomb were a popular material for nesting boxes in dovecotes. (See figure 9.5.)

Chalk continued in use as a building material until the beginning of this century. Most

quarries have now closed and defective stones are now usually replaced by salvaged blocks in conservation work.

9.5 Chalk-stone nesting boxes on interior wall of a dovecote at Uffington, Oxfordshire

9.6 Chalk-stone cottage at Woolstone, Oxfordshire

9.7 A new chalk wall with a bedding of hard cement-based mortar. This may encourage early decay of the chalk as shown in the example below (figure 9.8)

9.8 The hard mortar mix of the pointing has encouraged moisture to evaporate through the walling material. The surface has flaked off through the action of frost and left the mortar standing proud of the chalk

Ordinary chalk in building

Marsh Court, Stockbridge, Hampshire

This unique house, built of chalk, on the chalk landscape of the Hampshire downs was designed by EDWIN LUTYENS. Building took place from 1901 to 1904 and a ballroom was added in 1924. CHRISTOPHER HUSSEY writing in *Country Life* in 1932 describes it as a masterpiece ... 'it is a joyous expression of the materials of the locality, chalk, flint and tile – marshalled into large and simple shapes in harmony with the landscape. ... LUTYENS, versed in the lore of old country craftsmen, incorporated their learning into his architecture'. The house was built for HERBERT JOHNSON, a successful businessman; it is now a preparatory school.

Walls are of ordinary chalk blocks with a brick backing. Panels of black knapped flint in the form of chequer work, at the base of the walls, provide a practical solution to the problem of rainwater splash-back. A drum of flint is carried round the base of ground floor walls which have cellars below. Walls are protected by a good overhang at eaves level from a tiled roof except for the 'Elizabethan/ Tudor' section which has a parapet on the south front. Chimneys are of red brick.

Many of the interior features are of chalk including the massive carved chalk fireplaces in the great hall and the billiards room; the main reception hall has a delicately carved frieze with a design based on local wild flowers. When the house was being built a column of chalk, which was part of the geological formation, was left standing on the site; it was carved in situ to form a billiards table and the room was built around it. The table

9.9 Marsh Court Stockbridge, Hampshire, designed by Edwin Lutyens, built 1901–1904

9.10 and **9.11** Panels of knapped flint and chalk blocks at Marsh Court, Stockbridge

9.11

was topped with a slab of slate and a strip of marble, with a moulded profile, protected clothes from rubbing against the chalk. Sunken gardens, paved terraces and paths surround the house. Cottages and garden buildings on the estate are also of chalk.

The chalk is thought to have been hewn from a quarry, that has now been filled in, on the east side of the lane between Marsh Court and Stockbridge, (GORDON PEARSON). The presence of flints may suggest that the chalk was obtained from the hard lower beds of the Upper Chalk. Chalk for repair work has been obtained from a quarry at Houghton and also from Totternhoe.

The chalk blocks vary in size, with widths up to 24 in. (610 mm) or more and heights from about 6 to 15 in. (150 to 380 mm). Each block was limewashed on all faces at the time of building before being placed in a wall. A lime putty mortar with a hint of cement was used for the joints. It is slightly hard for this soft stone and although it has fared well on the north facing front there has been some deterioration on the southern side. Some stone has been replaced particularly on the upper section of walls not protected by eaves. Areas of wall have suffered near defective gutters and erosion of metal windows have caused spalling to mullions and transoms. Some of the LUTYENS' detailing to windows has complicated repair work; the frames were slotted into grooves in the chalk and sealed from the top.

The garden architecture has fared less well than the main house. This may be due to siting too near to large trees and to less care over detailing at the design stage. Where random stone has been mixed with chalk it has not been successful.

There is no record of limewash or other protective coats being applied to the walls of Marsh Court during the last 50 years or so. CHRISTOPHER HUSSEY writing in 1932 describes two forms of treatment to increase the imperviousness to moisture: '... the washing of the walls with milk. Though temporarily successful, it resulted in a skin of the surface flaking off at changes of temperature. The second, applied on the advice of Messrs HOLLAND, HANNEN and CUBITT, was the application of fluite crystals in solution. A preliminary application at 25 per cent of density was allowed to dry, then followed with a wash of 35 per cent of density. This has been found to afford complete impermeability, though probably the process should be repeated at intervals of ten years'. It might be argued that if the treatment had been continued sealing of the surface might not have allowed the chalk to breathe and the result might have been spalling of the surface. The chalk has remained remarkably white except for patches of algae and lichen which are mainly on the north facing wall or near rainwater pipes.

ACKNOWLEDGMENT

I gratefully acknowledge the help and information provided by:

MR ROGER BREALEY, Architect
MR BROADBENT, Marsh Court
MR PETER DARE, Master Mason
MR GOWEN DITCHBURN, Builder
MR JOHN MCCANN
MR GORDON PEARSON, Hampshire County Council
MR KEVIN STUBBS, Hampshire County Council.

10 FLINT

The nature of flint

Flint, which is composed of about 98 per cent pure hydrated silica, is an almost indestructible material and possibly unsurpassed by any other in its resistance to weathering. It has a hardness greater than that of steel yet is brittle and, in the hands of an experienced knapper, can be easily broken along the natural line of fracture.

10.1 Flushwork. The Gatehouse, St Osyth's Priory, Essex

There has always been an abundant supply of flint from the chalk deposits of the southern and eastern counties of England in the belts stretching from Norfolk, Canterbury and Eastbourne to Dorset. Flint buildings in these areas are said to be more numerous than anywhere else in the world.

The best quality flint gives the appearance in the mass of being a uniformly opaque, black and homogeneous material; this, however, is an optical effect. The material will splinter into fine flakes and these splinters, when held to the light, are translucent and of an almost colourless grey or yellow. When examined microscopically flint is found to be composed of minutely crystalline silica (often including silicified sponge-spicules and fragments of shells, sea urchins and other marine organisms) together with varying amounts of water, all formed around a nucleus. The fracture phenomenon reveals barely visible concentric rings of a shell-like or conchoidal character when resulting from a blow.

The exterior surface of the dark core is covered with a white crust or 'cortex'; this may be thin and transparent or several inches (centimetres) thick. A protective skin or 'patina' coating the cortex is basically white when extracted from the chalk but may be stained yellow, brown or other colours when in contact with minerals such as iron and manganese.

At Grime's Graves, on the Norfolk–Suffolk border, about 5 miles (8 km) north west of Thetford is an area of ground covered by hundreds of circular depressions marking the sites of flint mines dating from Neolithic times. One such pit, in the care of the Department of Education and Science, has been excavated and it is possible to descend about 30 ft (9 m) into the shaft to see the strata of chalk and flint with the radiating galleries at its base.

The purest and most sought after 'black-faced' flint, known as *floorstone* or *tabular flint*, was found at the lowest level. This has a fine texture and flakes cleanly; it was particularly valuable both in prehistoric times for weapons and tools and in the later Middle Ages for strike-a-lights and gun flints. Flint nearest the crust of a nodule was the best for these implements and the discarded core, called the *builder*, was used in the construction of a knapped flint wall; many of the cottages in the Brandon area are faced with this material. The stratum above the floorstone is known as *wallstone*; this flint flakes well and is suitable for knapped building work. Flint of the upper stratum tends to contain frost fractures resulting from the Ice Age; it is less suitable for knapping and is used in the form of nodules for building.

At the beginning of the century *builders* were categorized as:

1 Square black-faced builders
2 Square mixed coloured builders
3 Round black builders
4 Round mixed coloured builders
5 Random faced builders
6 Rough builders
7 Land stones.

The characteristics of flint in building are manifold. Rubble cored walls were faced with unfractured nodules of irregular shapes, sometimes complete with cortex, or roughly fractured stones as picked up from a field; these were pressed haphazardly into the surface of a thick plaster. Carefully selected rounded stones, often water smoothed, or those with amorphous shapes, were set coursed, or roughly coursed, within a wall. Knapped flint was mainly for the more sophisticated building with flushwork and proudwork reserved for the most important.

Dating flint buildings

The massive flint rubble walls of the Romans were laced with courses of tile-like bricks and faced, in some cases, with whole or split flints. Saxon and Norman work shows a predominance of mortar with fragments of brick, stone-rubble and unfractured nodules of flint scattered haphazardly in the face of the wall. Thirteenth-century walls tend to be roughly coursed; the proportion of mortar to stone is decreased and some of the flint nodules are fractured; walls faced entirely with split flints are rare before the 1290s.

Fourteenth-century walls may be distinguished from earlier work by the neater coursing. As walls ceased to be limewashed or rendered externally the appearance of the wall became more important. Knapped work, with flints roughly squared but of irregular sizes, is common in superior buildings: 'flushwork', where knapped flints are set into dressed stone to form decorative panels appears in the 1320s and chequer patterns are introduced in the latter part of the century. Flint in fifteenth-century walls is carefully graded and coursed in the better work; oval flints are set upright or slanted in courses and chequer patterns tend to be smaller and finer in prestigious buildings than those of the previous century. Flush tracery (figures 10.2 and 10.3) reaches its zenith in the second half

10.2 Squared knapped flints in flushwork at St Osyth's Priory

10.3 Split, unsquared nodules in flushwork. The south porch, Chelmsford Cathedral

of the fifteenth century and is seldom seen after the middle of the sixteenth century except for a brief revival that occurs in the nineteenth century.

Fine flintwork remained throughout the sixteenth century; the bands and panels of alternate stone and flint were not only decorative but also provided a means of strengthening the wall. Flint was a fashionable material in the Regency period and the Victorians, with their passion for polychrome effects, used it in conjunction with brick and stone to form stripes, diamonds and other patterns.

Dates and the initials of the knapper or builder can sometimes be seen incised in the flint.

The knapping process

The word *knap*, according to the *Oxford Dictionary*, is derived from the German and Dutch *knapen* to crack or snap. To strike with a hard short sound; to knack, to knock, to rap.

Flint used fresh from a chalk bed flakes more predictably than that from a clay bed. In Sussex the best flints for knapping are called *virgin flints*, ie those newly extracted from chalk pits; these are known locally as *Sussex diamonds*[1] because the minute crystallites of silica within the material are said to sparkle in the sun after a storm. Beach cobbles are also 'soft' enough to knap if newly gathered[1] but there is 'a job to get the start to play, ie the difficulty of getting a firm hold on the rounded flint to smash the first flake off'.[2]

When left exposed the flint may 'sweat', not through condensation but by evaporation of moisture within.[2] When too dry the material becomes unworkable and will shatter and fragment on knapping. Flint subjected to too much rainfall may become 'greasy' and difficult to handle. Craftsmen stress the importance of protecting the material awaiting use; a simple method is to cover the flint with a sheet of metal to ensure that plenty of air is able to circulate.[3]

Colours of flint vary in different areas; that from the Holt area in Norfolk is light grey whilst dark flint comes from Ramsgate. Most knappers have their own sources of supply. Flint suppliers are listed at the end of the chapter. Beach pebbles can only be obtained from a firm with a licence to supply.

A gentle blow in the correct position will sever a flint quite easily, whereas a hard blow at a random spot may produce no result. An experiment carried out using a magnum stone-splitter suitable for splitting granite showed that flints would not split in this way, they only shattered.[4]

By tapping a nodule, an experienced knapper is able to judge from the sound the best way to strike the material through the section of minimum toughness. A clear ring or 'zing' indicates a flawless flint; a dull thump or 'thack' shows a fault within.[2] Mr Avery of Brandon[3] is able to judge from the sound and demonstrate with a pencil line the exact position where a break will occur. Knappers can also judge where to deliver a blow without sounding the stone.

The knapper works with his wrist and the wrist is kept light. The flint nodule is held in the hand or steadied on the knee. Knapping hammers used in the past had tapered hexagonal heads and weighed from 3 to 7 lb (1.361 to 3.175 kg). Mr Baker of Southwick, in Sussex,[1] uses ordinary 'softish' iron hammers that have been 'blacksmithed', ie heated by a blacksmith to rid the iron of 'hardness'. He considers steel hammers too harsh for the material and cites examples where bricklayers have been injured using lump or club hammers. A true knapper, using the correct tools, does not require protective clothing.[1] The knappers employed by T Couzens and Sons of West Marden, West Sussex, have used bolsters and steel hammers for splitting chalk

10.4 Knapped and squared flintwork with galleting. Norfolk

flints but would not use this method on clay flints which are more brittle.

Mr John Lord, custodian of Grime's Graves, is able to make flint implements, following similar methods of preparing and shaping the material to those used by prehistoric man. For this precise work he finds a steel hammer too severe by reason of its greater concussive force and believes it to be no more effective than using more primitive methods. He uses the antler of a red deer for much of the work where striking or pressure flaking is required; this causes less damage to the flint surface than modern tools and makes easier the task of following the natural grain of the flint nodule. A flint hammer stone, he finds, is not suitable; flint against flint can cause both to snap. Where abrasion is required he uses a piece of sandy quartz stone or limestone which has a density approaching that of horn.

The sequence of making an arrow head or dagger, after the initial shape has been roughly set, is to chip or snap the edge to the required shape using a small piece of horn, then to grind the margin down with an abrasive stone. After forming a platform in this way he delivers a hard, sharp blow at a precise spot on the upper edge of the flint which dislodges a flat flake of the correct thickness from the underside. If a small lump remains on the surface it is removed by using a punch action with the aid of a mallet; to remove small scale-like flakes all that may be required is pressure from another stone. This work, although of a specialized nature, outlines the principles used for the process in building work.

Square knapping is the ultimate knappers art.[1] The sign of good knapping for building is an absolutely flush face. Squared flints are set close together in a wall with only a thin course of mortar visible on the face; this requires precise measurements with the use of a template. Dimensions may be up to 6 × 6 in. (150 × 150 mm) or more depending upon the quality and size of the flint.[1] FRED AVERY[3] uses a lead pencil to draw squares, normally 2 × 2 in. (50 × 50 mm), on the split face as a guide to dressing the flint. It takes him about one hour to knap 20 square-faced flints. There is an average of 70 per cent wastage of material. In Sussex, the unwanted flakes, known as *bangaroush*, are used as a filling for the core of the wall; smaller flakes are used for *gallets* (perhaps from the word *galet* French 'pebble') or *garnets*, or, in Sussex, *garrets*.[1] Gallets are both decorative and useful; they are inserted into the mortar and tighten the joints; they also direct water away from the mortar (see figures 10.4 and 10.5). Gallets do, however, tend to loosen with time and may often be seen scattered at the base of a wall. The price for unsquared knapped flints in 1984 was about £10.00 per square metre plus VAT.

Building with flint

The process of constructing a flint wall is slow and therefore expensive; a large quantity of mortar is required to fill the interstices between the irregular shaped stones and each section is allowed to set thoroughly to prevent bulging. An average day's work, depending upon the weather and its effect on the drying of the mortar, may be 1 square yard (0.8361 m^2) for repair work. For lengths of walling, four courses,[1] or a 12 in. (305 mm)[3] rise is normal. Work is not possible in wet or frosty weather.

The importance of the mortar mix is critical. Too much cement can create problems

10.5 The sandstone walling has weathered back leaving the flint galleting projecting in front of the face of the wall

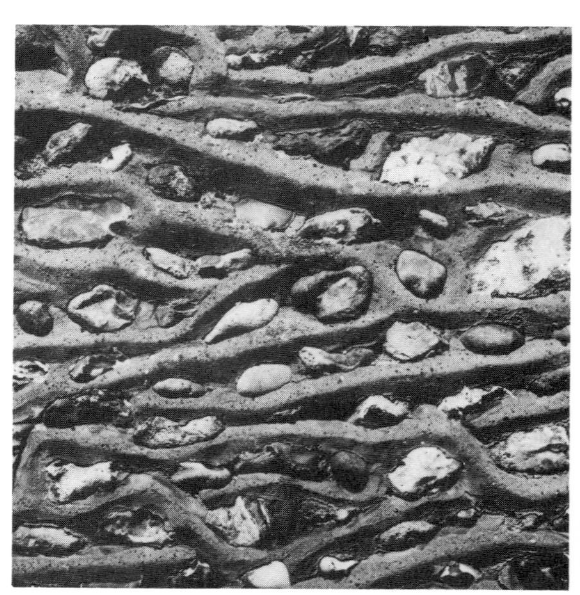

10.6 The character of the flint wall of a fine old Suffolk church has been destroyed by the raised pointing

and the water content needs to be just right as flints are unable to absorb moisture.[4]

Flint walls are often disfigured by modern cement pointing; water penetrating through shrinkage cracks in the dense impervious mortar is unable to evaporate and erosion may follow; soft mortar below hard will push off the hard outer skin fairly soon. A Portland cement-based mortar is difficult to remove; ideally the mortar should be allowed to decay and fall out with time; a hammer and chisel, if used, is likely to dislodge flints during the process (figures 10.6 and 10.7).

10.7 Uncoursed flint nodules with the mortar suitably recessed but spoilt by the hard cement-based mortar repair on the right hand side which is already displaying fine cracks sufficient for the ingress of water

It is of interest to note that FRANK BAGGALLAY writing in 1885 on the use of flint in building says that the white coat of flint should be 'broken off with a "napping" [*sic*] hammer; this, if not removed, turns the mortar joints yellow'. None of the building craftsmen interviewed considered this significant where lime mortar is used. It may be that BAGGALLAY's opinion assumed the use of cement mortar.

Mortar mix The lime mortar must be stiff enough to prevent the flints rolling out of position; the consistency should be similar to creamy butter, firm but slightly sticky.[1] Sharp, well washed coarse sands and grits are used with the minimum amount of water. The choice of sand, in repair work, is dictated by the colour and texture of existing mortar; allowance is made for the new mortar to darken with weathering. Artificial colour additives have a tendency to fade. In the past mortars were occasionally coloured with soot, sea coal and brick dust. SALZMAN cites 'Smythys Duste for the black mortar to be made of, requisite for the leying of Flynte'. Sometimes old mortar can be crushed and reused if it is not salt contaminated and does not contain ash. The proportion of old mortar to coarse sand should not exceed 50 per cent.

Some of the mixes suggested were:

(a) for facework repairs
1 lime:4 sharpish flinty sand of $\frac{3}{16}$ mm composition and a little cement to allow the lime to 'go off';[1]

(b) for bedding in repair and new work
$\frac{1}{4}$ cement:$1\frac{1}{2}$ lime:1 sand:5 grit;[5]

(c) a mix used for the repair of the ancient city walls at Norwich
$\frac{1}{6}$ Portland cement:1 Totternhoe lime: $2\frac{1}{2}$ sharp sand;[6]

(d) for repointing old walls that have a soft sandy core
1 cement:3 lime:12 sand graded with very coarse grit to 6 mm.[7]

In the past, an oft quoted specification for mortar for flint walls in East Anglia was hydrolized hydraulic lime and sand without the addition of cement; the shrinkage was minimal. Cement rich mortars tend to shrink and develop fine cracks. This lime from the

East Anglian Cement Company is no longer available. Hydrated hydraulic, or semi-hydraulic, lime would be similar today.

Method Shuttering for building a flint wall is not considered good practice; a line is preferred as it is essential to be able to see the face of the wall as work proceeds.

In repair work rake out loose material, remove any vegetation and flush out with clean water; avoid saturation.

New mortar is well compacted to prevent pockets of air forming; where cavities occur they may accumulate water. The dry flints are pressed into place by hand and care is taken not to disturb them when once in position. Keeping the face of the wall clean and flush and preventing mortar from bulging out is a difficult task and forms part of the art of building with flint.[1]

10.8 Uncoursed flint nodules with mortar recessed to avoid 'feather edging'. Norfolk

Filling joints Joints, if dry, are wetted before mortar is inserted. The finish of the joint is dictated by any surviving sections in the old wall or by local custom. A rubbed-back face with the flint showing 'fair deck' is suitable.[8] (See figure 10.8.) Mortar should not encroach over the flints. Pointing was rare before the Regency Period.

After the initial set of the mortar, granules of sand and grit are exposed to match surviving work; laitence is also removed at this stage. Timing is critical and varies according to the mix and weather conditions but will normally take place at the end of the day.

Suggested methods include:

(a) *Filling the joints:* the joints are rubbed round just as the mortar is 'turning' and the surface starts to crumble; a short length of hose pipe makes a useful tool for this purpose. After a further interval a stiff bristle brush is used to expose the fragments of grit on the surface. The removal of laitence is normally only necessary with flushwork; a damp cloth is used for this purpose.[8]

(b) *The 'rubbed sack' method:* an old sack is used to rub the surface in order to rid it of surplus mortar and provide the required texture.[5]

(c) For repair work to the city wall at Norwich the surface is sprayed lightly with a fine jet before the initial set takes place; it is then gently brushed with a soft hand-brush to remove any laitence and to expose the fine granules of sharp sand.[6] Cleaning the face of flints with linseed oil will attract dust and dull the surface.

Variations in the use of flint in walls

Water-rounded flints and those of irregular shapes, both knapped and unknapped, are laid *coursed, roughly coursed* or *uncoursed.* Some are set in broad courses and others are grouped close together with mortar barely visible on the face of the wall.

An uncoursed wall, particularly where formed of small nodules, can be deficient in strength. Bonding flints, through stones or bricks tailed deeply into the core at intervals will strengthen a wall; these need not necessarily be apparent on the surface. Flints laid as headers, with broadest sides outwards, provide a closer and firmer joint on the face. A wall may also be stronger and more damp resistant if no two flints touch and a minimum of $\frac{1}{2}$ in. (12 mm) is left between stones[9] (figures 10.14 and 10.15).

10.9 Coursed flints on a wall in Chichester, Sussex. The dark fragments of glass form a decorative feature and sparkle in the sunlight

10.10 Coursed flint in a Sussex wall

10.11 Roughly squared knapped flints laid uncoursed. Suffolk

10.12 Roughly squared knapped flints approximately coursed. Suffolk

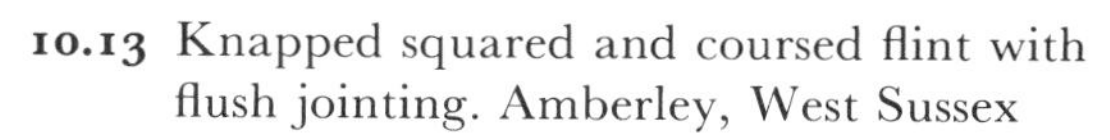

10.13 Knapped squared and coursed flint with flush jointing. Amberley, West Sussex

10.14 Flint galleting split flint courses and stone galleting in the limestone bands

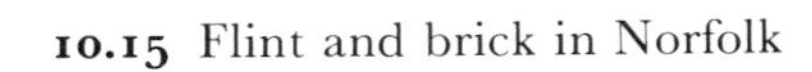

10.15 Flint and brick in Norfolk

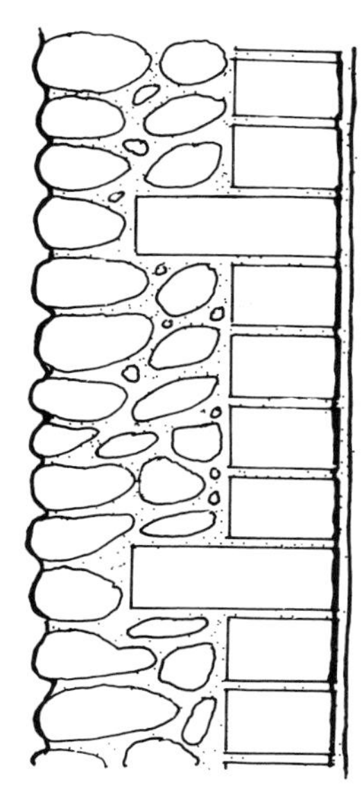

10.16 Section through a new flint wall with a brick backing

10.17 A knapped flint has become detached from the shallow bedding in part of a quatrefoil frieze. St Osyth's Priory Gatehouse

Brick, dressed stone or chalk used for quoins, eaves, plinths and jambs provided greater rigidity. Lacing courses and chequers in contrasting materials were both decorative and functional. Brick bonders commonly replaced every fourth, sixth or eighth flint.

A modern practice is to build a new flint wall with a brick backing; a 4½ in. (114 mm) brick inner skin with brick headers built into the core at intervals will provide the necessary bond (figure 10.16). Stainless steel ties used every two or three courses give a good key.[8] Brick piers at approximately 60 in. (1520 mm) intervals contribute extra strength.

In knapped work, and in particular flushwork, the shallow bedding of the flint can give rise to a weakness (figure 10.17). Flints may become detached and, when replaced, should be well tailed into the body of the wall using a weak lime-based mortar.

In constructing flushwork, the ashlared stone is cut to form decorative panels and the interstices are filled with flint, knapped or unknapped, set in mortar. In some cases the patterns are hollowed out of the stone to receive the flint, and the depth of the rebates, especially near the edges, can be as little as 1 in. (25 mm). It may be necessary to deepen the recess to provide a better key for the flint (figure 10.2).

Chalk was the traditional material used as a backing for flushwork and other knapped work as a means of absorbing moisture.[10] In some Victorian buildings there is a weakness in joints between the brick and flintwork leading to damp problems. This is due to poor bonding between the materials and is perhaps exacerbated by the non-porous nature of nineteenth-century bricks. Chalk or other limestone is usually more suitable with flint.

10.18 Distribution of flint, chert, cobbles, pebbles and boulder stones in walling

Gallets are pressed firmly into mortar, with a gloved hand, just before the initial set. They are set facing downwards and outwards.

FLINT SUPPLIERS

Chic-Grit Limited, Unit 12, Industrial Estate, Norwich Road, Watton, Norfolk

Howes Lime Sales Limited, Rougham Industrial Estate, Bury St Edmunds, Suffolk, IP30 9ND

Brandon Lime Company, Taflins Quarry, Santon Downham, Brandon, Suffolk.

ACKNOWLEDGMENT

I gratefully acknowledge the information provided by the building craftsmen listed below.

[1] Mr PDH Baker of Southwick, West Sussex

[2] Mr John Lord, Custodian of Grime's Graves, Norfolk

[3] Mr Fred Avery of Brandon, Suffolk

[4] Mr David Heap and Mr Webster of Civil Engineering Developments, West Thurrock, Essex

[5] Mr HA Jones of T Couzens and Son, West Marden, West Sussex

[6] Mr Robert Memess, Planning Officer, City of Norwich

[7] Caroe, Alban and Martin, *Stonework – Maintenance and Surface Repair*, published by the Council for the Care of Churches 1984

[8] Mr David Lodge of Stebbing, Great Dunmow, Essex

[9] Mr Spinks, Thetford, Norfolk

[10] Mr English of Brandon, Suffolk

FURTHER READING

See *Select bibliography* under '*Stone*' page 166.

11 PEBBLES, COBBLES AND BOULDER STONES

11.1 Barn at Bootle, Cumbria. Walls of cobbles ('cobble-ducks') with the corners reinforced with boulder stones

Pebbles, cobbles and boulder stones are the consequence of water action on a variety of rock types ranging from soft chalk-stone to granite. These water-rounded stones were collected from beaches (known in the Bootle area of Cumbria as *cobble-ducks*), river beds (known in the Lake District as *Beck stones*), streams or from the boulder clay (often referred to as *field stones*), where they were transported by glacial action during the Ice Age. They formed an endless supply of cheap building material for houses, cottages, farm buildings and field walling.

Pebbles are usually less than 3 in. (75 mm) in diameter and the sizes of cobblestones range from diameters of approximately 3 to 12 in. (75 × 300 mm). Boulder stones can be

11.2 Detail of the barn at Bootle

11.3 A chalk boulder wall, Flamborough, Humber

11.4 The dense, hard mortar pointing of this chalk boulder wall hinders evaporation of moisture. The chalk acts as a sponge and the wall is unacceptably damp

11.5 The Lake District. Beck stones from a local stream with slate levelling. The stones are laid in diminishing sizes from the base upwards. Throughstones, which include beckstones, span the thickness of the wall at intervals

of giant proportions. Pebbles are usually laid in walls in neat courses. Cobbles and boulder stones, which tend to be of irregular shape, are more often set random, or only roughly coursed, with the sizes of the stones graded so that the largest are placed at the base of the wall. The thickness of the wall also diminishes from the base to top. The largest stones are used for 'through stones', corner stones, foundations, plinths and lintels.

11.6 A barn at Skeffling, Humber

11.7 Detail of boulder stones and brickwork of the barn at Skeffling

11.8 A boulder walled cottage at Easington, Humber

11.9 Section through a boulder wall at Easington, Humber

11.10 A cottage at the Farming Museum, Auchindrain, Strathclyde, with walls constructed of local boulder stones

Boulder and cobblestones are wedged close together with fragments of stone or slips of slate used as lacing courses. Pebbles are always set in lime mortar throughout the thickness of the wall but cobblestones and boulder stones rely upon their bulk and construction, using through stones for their stability, and the mortar (sometimes recessed to give the appearance of dry stone walling) plays a less crucial role. Field walls are generally laid 'dry', ie without mortar.

12 LAKE DISTRICT MASONRY

12.1 Dry stone walling at Ravonstonedale, Cumbria. The 'watershot' (throughstones) project beyond the face of the wall

I am indebted to Mr RAVEN FRANKLAND for providing most of the following information.

In the heart of the Lake District, buildings and field walls are constructed of random dry stone walls, *watershot* or *weathershot*, a technique unique to the region.

The simple appearance of these beautiful walls, which require minimal stone dressing, belies the complexity of the construction and the skill needed to build them. The walls are kept drained and dry in an area of exceptionally heavy rainfall and driving rain. Frosting within a wall is rare.

The stone is the hard, flat-bedded 'green-

12.2 A field barn at Askrigg, North Yorkshire

stone' slate obtained from local quarries – often the waste – in sizes ranging from very small pieces to blocks up to 36 in. (910 mm) long. Colours vary from shades of green to grey.

Construction

The faces of the walls are constructed of roughly dressed stone of irregular shape. The cavity between is known as the *hearting*. Although the walls of buildings look like field walls there are basic differences in construction.

Field walls are battered, buildings are plumb. Large flat 'throughstones' (throughs) span the thickness of the walls, in approximate courses, at vertical intervals of about 36 in. (910 mm). The throughstones strengthen the wall and help to support the hearting above. In field walls throughstones are laid dead level. In buildings they are laid to a tilt, or watershot, with a rise of from 2 to 2½ in. (50 to 62 mm) to every 12 in. (300 mm) of wall thickness. The first course of watershot throughs should be 36 in. (910 mm) above foundation and in a field wall the throughs, laid level, should be 21 to 24 in. (530 to 600 mm) above the foundation. Throughstones are not cut back on the exterior but allowed to project in order to throw water clear of the face of the wall.

The facing stones on each side of the walls are packed tightly together. It is important to 'cross the joints', ie the vertical joints should be staggered. In a building, the stones on the exterior face of the wall are set at the same angle as the throughstones, sloping outwards,

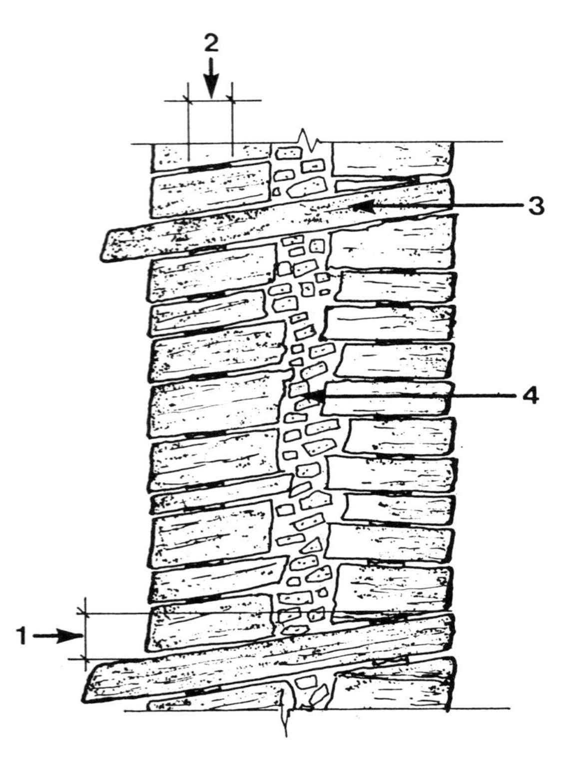

12.3 Watershot walling construction of buildings in the Lake District. The walls of buildings are watershot only on the external face, as shown in the above section. Field walls are watershot on both faces

1 Watershot (tilt) 4 to 5 in. (100 to 125 mm)
2 Mortar pointing set back 2 to 3 in. (50 to 75 mm)
3 Tilted throughstone (watershot stone)
4 Dry hearting

but for the internal face the stones are set level. Field walls are constructed with stones tilted outwards on both sides.

These stones, set to a tilt, drain water away from the core of the wall efficiently. Further, their durability is increased by being laid at the same angle as their natural planes of cleavage, as in the quarry.

The 'dry' hearting (there is no mortar) is packed firmly with small fragments of stone to permit easy drainage via the throughstones below.

The stone is laid on a thin line of mortar which is compressed to form a stable bed. Most walls constructed with the watershot technique remain perfectly dry without pointing. But where mortar is used it is recessed about 3 in. (75 mm) back from the face and extends to a depth of a further 3 in. (75 mm) or more. The mortar is a soft lime/sand mix and the main reason for recessing the joint is to protect the mortar from the hard driving rain of the Lake District. An incidental result is that the dry stone walling appearance is also retained.

Foundations are set solidly in a trench with the largest stones placed level 'end in end out' across the wall. The thickness of a field wall decreases towards the top of the wall by approximately 10 in. (250 mm). The wall is topped with 'camming'. Camms are large stones which lie flat on top of the wall.

A dry stone waller uses a two-ended hammer, one end with a square edge and the other pointed, for dressing or breaking stone into usable pieces.

Wallers normally work in pairs but RAVEN FRANKLAND, who has built more than 1900 yards (1,737 m) of dry stone walling on his farmland which extends over more than 120 acres (48.5 hectares), maintains solo is equally good. 'Walling with two men is unnecessary, you can wall overhand (from one side of the wall), and when you are building a new wall you can walk round it.' A string is normally used to align a wall in a building. However, Mr FRANKLAND has found that aligning by eye can be satisfactory, although a string is needed for camming.

12.4 Projecting slate tabling, supported by boulder stones, provides protection to window and door openings to cottages and farm buildings

12.5 Applethwaite Church, Cumbria. The recessed mortar gives the wall the appearance of dry stone walling

13 CARSTONE

'Carstone' (Carr-stone or Car-stone) is the term used to describe the hardened ferruginous sandstone of the Lower Greensand. Iron oxide has imparted a warm chocolate-brown colour to the stone and it is sometimes referred to in Norfolk as 'burnt gingerbread stone'.

Narrow outcrops of Greensand appear to the north and west of the chalklands of East Anglia; also in parts of the Weald. Carstone is found in abundance, at various depths, in West Norfolk. It is sandwiched between layers of sandy or chalky clay and divided vertically into rhomboidal blocks.

Just north of Downham Market the Greensand is exposed beneath a scarp and Carstone was easily obtained from here close to the surface; pieces are still picked up by farmers when deep ploughing their fields. Surface pits are thought to have existed for centuries at Downham Market, Bexwell, West Dereham, Shouldham and Blackborough.[1] Carr from Snettisham quarry, near Downham Market, was extracted from beneath a layer of red chalk at a depth of 7 ft (2.1336 m) below ground level. The upper 60 in. (1524 mm) of Carstone was loose rubbly stone; beneath this a 15 ft (4.5720 m) solid layer yielded stone that could be used in the form of large blocks for building.

13.2

13.1 and **13.2** Downham Market, Norfolk

13.3 Carstone slips

13.4 Carstone blocks

The principal quarry at Snettisham is reputed to be more than a thousand years old, according to Mr JW MESSENT in his book *A Thousand Years of Norfolk Carstone*. The quarry provided most of the Carstone for building within a 12 mile (19 km) radius; it has continued in use intermittently until the present time.

Carstone is soft and friable when first removed from the quarry and can easily be dressed at this stage; the stone hardens on exposure and becomes a good durable building stone that will withstand damp and exposure.

Downham Market, Norfolk

Carstone is the prevalent material for old buildings in Downham Market. The houses and cottages are interesting and of unusual construction. Most were built in the eighteenth and nineteenth centuries but a few date from the seventeenth century, and earlier walls are thought to be masked behind some of the existing façades. Panels of Carstone walling, using traditional techniques, have been introduced into some of the modern buildings.

13.5 A coursed Carstone panel in a brick wall

13.6 Downham Market

Rubbly Carr of the fissile kind, which could be easily split into small pieces, was laid coursed, or roughly coursed, with the mortar recessed (back bedded) which gives the appearance of dry-stone walling. Each stone was sloped gently downwards and outwards in order to shed water. The slips of stone are usually no more than 1 to 2 in. (25 to 50 mm) thick. The resulting wall has a very pleasing texture with the stone resembling 'chocolate bar pieces'.

The main façades are usually more neatly coursed than the other elevations. Side walls, particularly in nineteenth-century houses, are often brickwork. Most buildings have limestone dressings or, in later houses, dressings in red and yellow brick.

13.7 A modern Carstone panel

13.8 Roughly coursed random Carstone

Mr A S Brown, of Brown and Horton, builders at Downham Market, is one of the few people conversant with the traditional building techniques used in the construction of the old coursed rubble Carstone walls in the town. The cottages and houses are varied in style and unique in character; Mr Brown describes them as 'durable, solid and very warm; warmer than most modern homes built with cavity walls'. He has repaired many Carstone walls in the area and has revived the technique by incorporating Carstone in the walls of new buildings. I am grateful to Mr Brown for providing the following information.

Small quantities of Carstone of a suitable size for building can still be found in the sand of shallow pits in Downham Market and Denver. It is also still possible to buy large lumps of Carstone from the Hunstanton pits; this stone is heavily fractured and when hit with a hammer will split into small pieces ready for use. Salvaged stone is another important source of supply and was used by Brown and Horton when building the extension to the Roman Catholic Church in Howdale Road where they incorporated panels of Carstone in the brick walls.

Mr Brown believes that the local practice of recessing the mortar behind the face of the stone was mainly for aesthetic reasons; 'it was probably a fashion. There are one or two examples in Downham Market where the mortar was finished flush with the stone but the appearance is not so good. There is no evidence of moisture penetration where the joints are recessed'.

Often an entire wall has been built in Carstone which eliminates the need for a plinth of another material. Many houses have brick or stone dressings to door and window openings, also 'ashleyes' at corners. The dressings are not an essential part of the construction, as with chalk or flint walls, but were mainly intended as a means of decoration. Brown and Horton have built columns of 36 in. (914 mm) diameter, at 15 ft (4.572 m) centres, at the Grammar School at Hunstanton using coursed Carstone without dressings.

The old walls are generally 13 to 18 in. (330 to 457 mm) thick overall. The coursed Carstone on the exterior face of the wall is bonded by through stones that project at intervals from a solid stone inner wall built of random rubble or brick. The core of the wall is filled with a rubble mix of odd bits of stone, brick or whatever could be found close to the site.

The slips of Carstone are bedded in mortar which is usually about $\frac{1}{4}$ in. (6.35 mm) thick. The mortar is recessed $\frac{1}{4}$ to $\frac{1}{2}$ in. (6.35 to 12.70 mm) back from the face of the wall and extends 3 to 4 in. (75 to 100 mm) into the core of the wall. Lime mortars were originally used and Mr Brown considers it important to use a similar mix when doing repairs. Brown and Horton use a lime:sand mix in proportions of 2:5 to which is added just a trace of cement.

Shuttering was not used in building a wall; the neat and precise appearance of the coursing was done by 'skilled craftsmen who did it by eye, although it is possible that some may have found a line helpful after constructing the "asleyes" at the corners'. Bonding was not considered necessary and would have spoilt the random character of the wall.

When Brown and Horton built the Carstone panels for the extension to the Roman Catholic Church they used neither line nor shuttering. Wall ties were used in this instance to bond the Carstone to a brick backing. 'It was a very slow process', says Mr Brown, 'but the result is gorgeous.'

Although old Carstone walls are very durable and most look as good as they did when first built, it occasionally happens that a piece of stone will become detached from the mortar of the back bedding; for example where a child has kicked a part of the wall. Brown and Horton sáy that it is essential to repair the wall immediately because if one stone becomes loose, a domino effect can be created and other stones around it may also fall out.

REFERENCE

Messent, J W, *A Thousand Years of Norfolk Carstone*, 1967.

14 STONE SLAB FIELD WALLING

14.1 Shard walling at Hawkshead, Cumbria

I am indebted to Mr PHILLIP BARR, of The National Trust, North West Region, Building Department, for the following information.

Hand-riven slate-stone slabs set vertically to form field walls are still occasionally seen in slate areas, notably Scotland, North Cornwall, North Wales and parts of the Lake District. Most of these walls are bedded at the base in the earth and pinned together near the head with a line of heavy wire strapping. The 'shard' walling of the Hawkshead/Ambleside areas of Cumbria is similar in principle but different in character and construction in that the slabs interlock and there is, therefore, no need for wire strapping.

The slabs are set in the ground to a uniform height, typically 36 in. (900 mm) above ground level. In most walls the head of each slab is dressed to the level; in other walls the

14.2 Detail of shard walling showing interlocking slabs

levelling is only approximate. There are considerable variations in widths. The bedded depth of a slab is related to its height and is generally about 18 to 20 in. (450 to 500 mm) below ground level, ie approximately one-third of the total length of the slab.

The heads of most of the slabs are carefully dressed to a shallow bevel, whereas the edges are only roughly dressed to form, at each junction, an interlocking system in alternate planes, making a closely knit joint (figure 14.2). Dressing, with a hammer and chisel, was probably done on site.

The stone is a shaley slate rock with an irregular surface, said to belong to the Upper Silurian System. Similar stone is obtained from a quarry at Borwick Ground, Cowper.

The stone is almost indestructible when set in a vertical plane but it is not durable when laid horizontally, ie against the bedding plane (the reverse to normal). Shard walling requires little maintenance. It is resistant to all but the heaviest impact. Sheep never scale these walls as they frequently do in the case of dry stone walling.

Phillip Barr has carried out documentary research into the origins of these walls and the people who built them, but has so far not been able to reach any definite conclusions. He believes that they were first built not earlier than 1400, but certainly before the period of the Enclosure Movement in the eighteenth century. They may have been connected with the monks of Hawkshead.

Mr Barr points out that local building terms usually have a straightforward meaning and describe the task they perform; for instance, *wrestlers* are interlocking slates at the ridge of a roof; *watershot* describes the function of the sloping throughstones that drain

14.3 Shard walling

the core of a wall; *tabling* refers to a projecting horizontal slate or stone course, like a table, above a window or the top of a gable.

The *Oxford Dictionary of English Etymology* describes *shard* as . . . 'gap; fragment of broken earthenware . . . (pot*sherd*), OE, *sćeard*, corresponding to Old Frisian *skerd* cut, notch . . .'.

'As a starting point for further research', says PHILLIP BARR, 'some correlation might be established between areas in which *shard* is used and where notching is the method of joining.'

15 WATTLE AND DAUB

Wattle

Post and wattle construction has been used for exterior walls and internal partitions since Romano-British times and a similar method was employed by the Ancient Egyptians. Timber posts or stakes were interwoven with branches, twigs, reeds or thin slats of wood in the manner of basketwork. This weft of wattlework provided adequate support, and formed a good key for the thick coats of daub that were applied to both sides of the framework.

15.1 Detail of wattle and daub
1 Riven oak stave slotted into the frame at both ends
2 Wattlework
3 Lime/sand render or coats of limewash
4 Daub

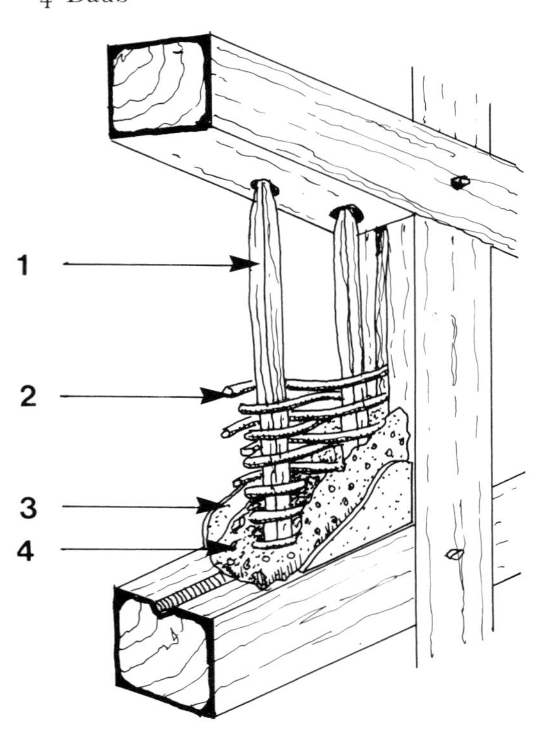

Wattle and daub (defined as 'interwoven twigs plastered with clay or mud, as a building material for huts, etc' in the *Shorter Oxford Dictionary*) was the most common type of infill for the panels between horizontal rails and vertical studs of timber-framed buildings. Construction followed similar patterns, with slight regional variations, throughout Britain. It was the simplest, and remains one of the most suitable methods of infill because of its flexibility. A timber frame is always prone to movement due to the wood expanding when damp and contracting when dry. The differential movement between an unyielding panel, such as brick nogging, and a timber frame, creates a habitual problem of repairing the ever-opening cracks around the edges of the panels. Wattle and daub moves with the building and if well maintained it could last indefinitely in moderate and sheltered conditions. Maintenance entailed no more than making good with a little mud patching from time to time and the annual bucket of limewash. Old panels seldom show cracks between panel and frame.

Materials for this construction were cheap and easily obtained. The usual wood was hazel which is light in weight, tough and pliable. Hazel withies were used for the weft (horizontal) and often for the vertical members as well. Clefts of oak, chestnut or beech and sticks of oak, alder, ash, holly or birch were also suitable for uprights.

Most of the hazel coppices that cover large areas of the South and South Eastern counties and the Midlands were planted artificially. Where there was an abundance of stone suitable for building houses and boundary walls hazel coppices were less common.

A hazel coppice was carefully controlled and only cut at seven to ten year intervals; tenants were able to claim timber for repair or for building from their landlords. Winter-cut hazel rods of about seven years' growth were considered best for wattle fences. The wood was used as soon as it was cut; if left it became difficult to use. In cold weather the 'green' rods were warmed over a fire to make them more malleable. (H L Edlin, *Woodland Crafts in Britain*, Batsford, 1949.)

Wattle panels of great age have survived; some of which are practically intact. In many cases the wattles were peeled of their bark before insertion into the frame. Stripping the bark may have rendered the wood less vulnerable to rot and insect attack.

The upright staves were sharpened to a point at one end and the other end was left blunt or chamfered. The pointed ends were slotted into holes at 6 in. (150 mm), or more, centres bored into the underside, or occasionally the topside, of the horizontal rails of the timber-framed building. The blunt end of the stave was sprung under compression into a recess or groove cut $\frac{1}{2}$ to 1 in. (12 to 25 mm) into the topside, or underside, of the horizontal timber member.

Hazel withies $\frac{7}{8}$ to 1 in. (22 to 25 mm) thick were woven horizontally between upright staves. The ends of the withies were normally secured by the end staves which were set close to the edge of the panel but sometimes they were slotted into grooves cut into the vertical framing. There were no nails, pieces of string or wire to keep the wattlework in place; where these are found they are likely to indicate later repairs.

Stud and mud was more usual than wattle and daub for close-studded panels where the width of the opening was narrow in relation to the height. L F Salzman cites examples in the fourteenth century (*Building in England Down to 1540*). Narrow cleft oak laths were slotted crosswise or upright into the panel opening. Bundles of reed (figure 15.2) or butt-edged boarding formed alternative backings. Daub was pressed into the interstices between the backing material to form a key. An alternative method was to work handfuls of the

15.2 Daub with reed backing. Redgrave, Suffolk

clay/straw mix into 'cats', or balls, to build up the render. The craftsmen who applied the daub were called *catters* or *daubers*. (NORMAN DAVEY, *A History of Building Materials*.)

15.3 and **15.4** Lath and daub

15.4

Daub is basically a mixture of clay, straw and cow dung but components and proportions varied according to the materials at hand. Straw, flax stems, reeds and other vegetable fibres or animal hair acted as binders to counteract shrinkage cracks as the clay dried out; they also helped to lighten the weight of the daub. Cow dung increased the strength of the mix and provided a degree of protection against damp penetration.

To apply the daub, two men stood either side of the wattle framework and threw handfuls of the mixture with full force against the wattling. The phrases 'slap in the eye' and 'mud in the eye' are said to have stemmed from this practice. The surface of the daub was smoothed, cracks filled in and the surface coated with limewash.

The porous nature of limewash allowed damp to evaporate from the wall. The addition of cow dung strengthened the limewash and imparted a good colour; fresh ox blood, copperas (ferrous sulphate) and earth pigments were among other colouring agents. Shredded tallow, linseed oil, skimmed milk or other ingredients were added to improve the weathering qualities of the limewash.

Repairs

The wattle framework

MR GEORGE BOURNE of Wychbold, Worcestershire, is a carpenter who specializes in the repair of old buildings using traditional techniques. He also works for the Avoncroft Museum of Buildings at Bromsgrove.

Hazel is readily grown in the area and Mr BOURNE says that people 'encourage its growth because it keeps down the weeds. Withies are usually made of hazel wood although willow is also used.

'Hazel rods $\frac{3}{4}$ in. (19 mm) round are split

down the middle using a *froe** for the cleaving and a *brake* (or break) to hold the work steady.'

Brakes do not conform to a standard pattern; they are constructed by craftsmen to suit their own needs. A brake in its simplest form is a stump of a tree with a cleft cut in it to hold a rod. The natural fork of a tree supported on three short legs serves the same purpose.

Mr Bourne's brake, that is used 'mainly for small stuff, is made up of three vertical posts, placed on the ground in the form of a triangle, with tree rails nailed over the top and fixed so that the top and bottom of each are just out of level. To split a rod the piece is wedged firmly within the brake at the point where two timbers meet. You have to use pressure on the handle of the froe to lever off the clefts; the rod is in tension and you turn it as the split extends down the centre. You can insert any thickness of timber; the natural split is at the thinnest point but as you want the split in the centre you place the thickest end downwards.

'You can also use a broad-bladed hedging hacker for cleaving hazel; the blade is inserted in one end and the hazel is twisted until it opens up. A simple brake is needed; this is made from two 3 in. (76 mm) posts with a rail across.

'Timber must be fresh; you cannot split old wood, and hazel should be used within two weeks of cutting. The smaller the section of timber the quicker it dries out but if the bark is on the moisture will not escape so quickly.

'After 100 years wattle becomes loose and loses its springiness. As it is touched it may fall to pieces. When a building is moved the wattlework nearly always needs to be replaced as in the case of Bromsgrove House at the Avoncroft Museum. Here the staves are of split oak 1½ in. (38 mm) wide and 1 in. (25 mm) thick with the sides split off like a very flat diamond. The distance between staves depends on the width of the panel; they are usually fixed at about 18 in. (450 mm) centres. A 40 in. (1020 mm) wide panel would have one stave in the middle and one on each side close to the studs. Wider panels might need closer spacing to keep the panel stiff.

'Each withy is cut close to the edges of the panel; they are not twisted and turned round the outer staves as in the case of hurdle making. There is no need for a groove in the vertical framing to form a stop for the withies.'

It is easy to imagine that a wattle mesh surrounded by damp daub, and without ventilation, would be subject to decay but George Bourne says this is not so and compares the damp mesh to timber that has lasted for centuries where it has been submerged under water or bogs.

Mr Richard Pailthorpe of the Weald and Downland Museum, Singleton in Sussex, says that it is easy to repair a wattlework panel with a little practice. The old pattern is followed; the hazel is used 'green' and should be cut from early October to May.

The Museum usually employs hurdlemakers for the work. There are still a number of these men in South East England; their skills are in demand for garden fencing as well as sheep hurdles.

* A *froe* is described in the *Shorter Oxford English Dictionary* as 'a wedge-shaped tool used for cleaving and riving staves, shingles, etc. It has a handle in the plane of the blade, set at right angles to the back'.

Daub

'There are as many daubs as there are daubers,' says Richard Harris, technical director of the Weald and Downland Museum at Singleton.

Heather Champion, a conservator at the Museum, describes the methods that she has used in daubing the wattle infill panels of buildings that have been re-erected at the Museum.

The old daub is matched where possible but the mix used in the original work follows regional variations and, even after careful soil analysis, precise reproduction can be difficult. Wealden clay is preferable to the chalky soil of Singleton. A clay sub-soil, which contains little or no organic matter, is suitable for daubing wattlework. All large stones are removed before use.

Traditional mix
6 earth (clay content maximum 15 per cent)
6 sharp sand
1 fresh cow dung
2 straw cut into 6 in. (15 mm) lengths.

Water is added in small quantities. If the mix is too dry it becomes crumbly and if it is too wet it is too heavy for the background. After the daub has been applied to the wattlework, or stud framing, the surface is worked and smoothed for the following four or five days. A float is used to fill any cracks that may develop as the daub dries out. Limewash, using freshly slaked lime with tallow incorporated, is applied to the exterior.

Weald and Downland Museum mix
1 earth (clay content maximum 15 per cent)
2 slaked lime
1 sand
3 kibbled chalk (granules of pea-sized chalk to give it bulk)
1 cut straw
Water to mix.

This is mixed to a fairly wet consistency and left for a few days before application.

Carol Manley was unable to find a local builder prepared, or even able, to use traditional materials and techniques to repair the daub infill panels of her fine timber-framed building in Kent. She decided to attempt the work herself.

She made some exploratory tests to find a daub that matched the original work. The old daub had a sweet smell that was difficult to analyse. She first tried using the local clay, together with a little cow dung and straw but the mix was prone to severe mould growth which she thought was due to the cow dung. 'Digging up clay from the garden was impractical,' said Mrs Manley, 'so I decided to try one of the brick earths that had been used by the Romans in Kent to make tiles. Colonel Dean of the brickworks at Sittingbourne became very interested and supplied dry brick earth at 50p a yard.

'A successful mix was obtained by reconstituting some of the old daub from damaged panels in the house and mixing it with the new brick earth. Brick earth is known to benefit from the action of frost so it can be left in winter to weather in the open. Because the straw in the old daub was thought to have become "dead", a quantity of new straw was fed into an old hand-operated chaff cutter. The mix of reconstituted clay, together with the new brick earth was piled in a heap on the ground and wetted using a watering can. Straw was spread in a layer on top and the mixture trodden in with the heels of gum-booted feet. Water and more straw were added at intervals. Old writings say that frequently turning in the mix with a shovel is of utmost importance. When the daub was sufficiently pliable and had a consistency rather like *Plasticine*, it was ready for use. It was important not to use the mix too wet; if it has become too wet either add more brick earth or leave it overnight to dry out a little. Only small quantities of daub should be prepared at a time as a large pile of the mix made very heavy turning. The elusive sweet smell was retained in the new daub.

'The most effective method of application was to fling handfuls of daub, with some force, down into the laths fixed between the stud framing, wearing rubber gloves. This helped the daub to penetrate between the laths and give a suction fit. I used laths $1\frac{1}{2}$ in. wide × $\frac{1}{4}$ in. thick (38 × 6 mm) and galvanized nails. The daub was finished with a wood float, and not overworked, which produced a soft, roughcast surface similar to the original. Any projecting straws were easily pressed back into the daub using the corner of the wooden float. A finer finish may be achieved once the clay has hardened up by soaking the float in water before working the surface.

'The daub has fared well. Any shrinkage on the edge of the panels on drying are filled with clay using a pointed trowel. Hairline cracks in daub plasters are filled by the subsequent limewash treatment. Large panels are more likely to suffer such cracks but they can be rubbed over with a handful of brick earth and worked in with a wet paint brush.

'New timber inserts may be toned down by rubbing wet brick earth into the grain of the oak and leaving it to dry. When it is wiped off, the oak will have become grey. It is not easy to distinguish the new work from the old – provided the carpentry is good!'

16 PARGETTING

Pargetting, pargeting: to daub with plaster. *Pargeter*: to throw or cast over a surface; from *par*: through, all over; and *jeter*: to throw or cast (*Shorter Oxford English Dictionary*). The term was formerly used to describe any type of basic rough-textured plaster or daub work, including the process used for lining a chimney. Today 'pargetting' refers to the decorative lime/hair plaster applied to exterior walls, and occasionally interiors, of timber-framed buildings or those built of clay lump or brick.

Pargetting is mainly associated with domestic architecture in South East England; notably North West Essex, South West Suffolk, South Norfolk, East Hertfordshire, Cambridgeshire and Kent. Old prints showing London prior to the Great Fire of 1666 depict timber buildings clad in decorative parge-work. There are also some fine examples of ornate work in York, Oxfordshire, Herefordshire, Devon and Somerset.

Raised parge-work in low relief, depicting carefully modelled subjects as created by the village craftsman, appears to have been a short-lived fashion. Surviving examples date from the mid-sixteenth century with the richest examples in the third quarter of the seventeenth century after which this method gradually fell out of favour. The walls of houses in towns and large villages, built by rich merchants, were adorned with boldly modelled parge-work. The designs were usually contained within panels which portrayed figures, animals, flowers, swags, coats

16.1 Lavenham, Suffolk

of arms or other items which were sometimes associated with the owner or his family. Simulated ashlar or quoinwork was fashionable. Inspiration is thought to have stemmed from the stucco duro of the Italian artists and their elaborate external panels on such buildings as Henry VIII's palace at Nonsuch.

Decorative incised work appears to have pre-dated and to have continued longer than the more sophisticated raised work. Designs were often complex on important seven-

16.2 Old and new work at Lavenham, Suffolk

teenth-century houses but by the eighteenth century patterns had become formalized and more uniform in character. During the nineteenth century plain roughcast became the typical form of protective render.

The practice of scratching and stamping the mortar while it was still wet was a means of compacting the plaster; a textured surface also helped to protect the plaster by breaking the rainfall.

Designs included squares, diamonds, zigzags, herring-bones, fans, basket-work and cables, together with more complicated motives using flowers, birds, insects and animals. Tools were usually basic and home-made. *Stickwork*, a form of incised pargetting, was achieved with the use of a pointed stick or a number of sticks tied together in the form of a fan. *Sparrow picking* was produced with the tip of a trowel or a piece of wood covered with spikes similar to, and perhaps derived from, a leggett as used by a thatcher to dress back water reed.

Hand-carved wooden moulds were used for

16.3 A variety of patterns on adjoining houses. Saffron Walden, Essex

16.4 Almshouses at Dedham, Essex. A fan of pointed sticks was often used to create patterns similar to the intersecting wavy lines shown here

16.5 Incised zigzag work. Essex

16.7 The metal comb is slotted, at its lower edge, into the hook of the wooden support and used for fan designs

16.6 Pargetting tools

16.8 Mould for indent chevron patterns

'butter pat' designs, such as scallops and fans, in repetitive indent work. Beeswax casts were a means of reproducing a particular motif. Cut template techniques were required for sunken borders, panels, strapwork, voussoirs and quoins; the wooden templates were placed in position before the final coat of plaster was applied and were removed when the top coat became sufficiently hard. Recessed areas were sometimes coloured to simulate mortar. Window and door architraves generally projected beyond the external face of the façade as a means of providing a stop for the plaster.

Pargetting was done by the village mason or plasterer. He used a mortar mix similar to that used for parging a flue consisting of a mix of lime, sand and cow dung together with road scrapings. Animal hair was incorporated as a binder and animal fat was added as further protection against the ingress of moisture. A harder, and less durable mix was used during the Victorian period for stamped work. Where limewash was applied this was tinted with the earth pigments of a particular area; there were Suffolk pinks, apricots and buffs, Kentish reds and Cambridge whites.

Very little original external pargetting sur-

16.9 A simple panel layout commonly used on buildings with regularly spaced windows. Thaxted, Essex

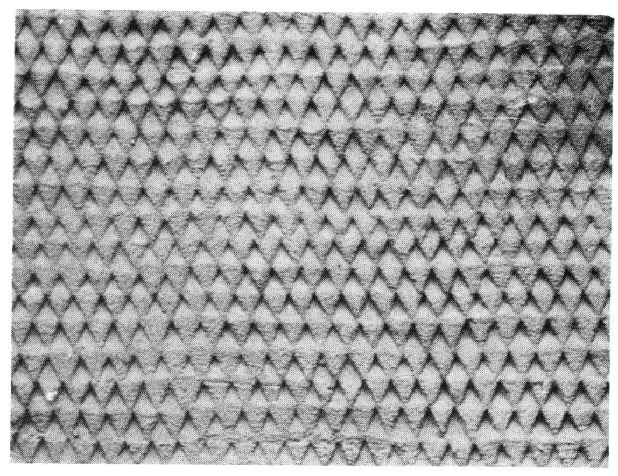

16.11 Recent pargetting near Nayland, Suffolk

16.10 Stratford St Mary, Essex

16.12 Early twentieth-century stamped work in Kent

vives although a few early fragments are sometimes discovered buried beneath multiple coats of limewash. Elaborate raised work has generally been restored over the years and much of the incised work has been copied in a hard mechanical manner using modern tools and unsuitable cement mortars. Interior pargework has fared better.

Lethaby notes that: 'In the eastern counties plasterwork repairs in out-of-the-way cottages still clumsily match the deft, old pattern work, which, after being perfected by hundreds of years, is now done no longer.' There is no longer a living tradition in decorative pargetting but there are a few good conservators who have perfected their own means of saving what remains of this ancient craft.

Construction

John Dives, a conservator and sculptor, was asked to repair the pargetting at Gifford's Hall, Stoke by Nayland in 1985. Part of the timber framing together with some of the infill panels had decayed. Due to the importance of this fine building, which dated from the fifteenth century, all new work had to be restricted to the absolute minimum.

Coats of old limewash had obscured much of the original pargetting. Mr Dives commenced by investigating an area measuring 12 in. × 5 in. (300 × 125 mm) to ascertain the form of the early designs impressed in the plaster; he used a spatula and scalpel and painstakingly removed layers of limewash to uncover the patterns. The next step was to take press moulds of the original pargework; for this he used potters' clay. He then transcribed the matrix to a piece of deal to form a more permanent mould for repeat pattern work.

The new plasterwork was supported on riven chestnut laths which had been prepared in the traditional way by Nick Cater of Margaretting, Essex. The laths were nailed to vertical timbers that were positioned behind the plane of the main timber framing. A space was provided between each lath sufficient to allow the plaster to be pressed in between and hooked over at the back.

For a large area of pargetting John Dives tackles the work in the manner of working on a fresco painting. He says pargetting is best done in panels and, as with fresco work, one should only plaster as much as can be completed in a day; once work has started it must be completed without a break.

The texture of the new plaster is important. For the mortar at Gifford's Hall the sand was sieved and the fine stuff was retained for the top coat. It was also essential to wash the sand to get rid of the brown (loam) colour. The lime used was from Buxton, Derbyshire. Goat hair was added as a binder; this arrived on site in matted bundles and had to be untangled by placing it in a wooden box and stirring hard with a large stick.

Plaster was applied in two coats with the base coat of rough cast. The composition of the mortar for the base coat was 3 sand : 1 lime with some goats' hair teased into the mix. The mortar was floated and squeezed between the laths; it was sprayed with water prior to floating the top coat. Continued spraying helped mortar to crystallize. Before the mortar went off the surface was scraped with a piece of wood or a trowel to form a rough and gritty texture which would provide a key for the next coat. A slightly richer mix was used for the top coat; 2½ sand : 1 lime together with a small quantity of goat's hair.

A thin fatty skin forms on the surface of the floating coat. Mr Dives says it is essential to know the precise moment that one is able to impress the skin to form a pattern without breaking the film; if it is left too long the surface will go slightly gritty. Pargetting over

16.13 Sparrowe's House, Ipswich

16.14 A recently repaired panel at Sparrowe's House

brickwork poses greater problems as the brick absorbs moisture from the mortar.

Mitres formed at corners of panels require particular care. A timber mould is used and once in position it must be gently tapped and kept moving if joint marks are to be avoided.

JOHN DIVES considers that limewash will dull a sharp pattern and discourages its use.

MR JOHN FORD CRP MPCS says that the Ancient House, known locally as *Sparrowe's House*, in the Buttermarket at Ipswich has some of the finest modelled and carved parge-work in the country. The decorative work is mainly at first floor level on the elevations overlooking two streets and part of the internal courtyard. Figures, animals, birds, foliage and buildings adorn plaster areas between and above the windows.

Sparrowe's House is thought to have been completed around 1601. By the time the local council had acquired this Grade I listed building in 1980 it was in a bad state of decay and required considerable repair to the structure and to the parge-work. Mr JOHN FORD of Ipswich was invited to conserve the pargetting; this was carried out over a 2½ year period and was completed in 1985.

All original work was retained where possible but in areas where decay was substantial loose material had to be taken back to the laths. It was necessary to replace rotted timber laths with galvanized expanded metal laths as a means of economy.

The mortar mix of the existing parge-work was analysed and the new work was matched where practicable. The original intention had been to use slaked lump lime, following traditional methods, but when work started the lump lime was found to have too many impurities which proved not to be suitable for building out the front mouldings. The lump lime was therefore changed to hydrated lime.

The composition of the mortar used in the repair work was: 1 part lime: 1 part silver sand; 10 portions of this were then mixed with 1 part HTI (high temperature insulation) powder. JOHN FORD found that this mix worked well for both the decorated external plasters and the plain-faced internal plasters. Goats' hair was added to the base-coat to act as a binder; proportions were 3 lb (1.36 kg) of hair to 1 cu yard (0.764 cu metres) of plaster.

Plaster was mainly two-coat work but for moulded work a third coat was required to provide the necessary thickness. The base-coat was left for a couple of days until nearly dry before the top-coat, composed of a slightly finer mix, was applied. The base of the design work was lightly modelled before carving. The finished work was limewashed. In some areas Mr FORD had only the barest trace of contours to guide him but he succeeded in re-creating work that blended with the spirited designs of the original.

ACKNOWLEDGMENT

I gratefully acknowledge the help and information provided by the following conservators and building craftsmen:

MR W A BRAY, Ashwell, Hertfordshire
MR JOHN DIVES, Whyteleafe, Surrey
MR MARTIN DOLAN, Ipswich
MR JOHN FORD, Ipswich
MR T JACKSON, Saffron Walden, Essex.

FURTHER READING

See *Select bibliography* under '*Pargetting*' page 168.

17 MATHEMATICAL TILES

Mathematical tiles (also known as *brick-tiles*, *rebate tiles* or, in the eighteenth century, *weather tiles*) are a form of interlocking tiles which were fixed vertically on a wall as a cladding in the eighteenth and nineteenth centuries. The tiles were intended to simulate bricks and it is often difficult to distinguish between a wall built of bricks and one clad in mathematical tiles.

Their use appears mainly in the South Eastern counties. The greatest number of buildings clad in the tiles are in Sussex, with a high concentration in Brighton and Lewes, and in Kent particularly in areas around Canterbury and Faversham. There are also some in central Surrey, parts of Wiltshire and Hampshire, including the Isle of Wight, and a few isolated examples in London, Norfolk, Suffolk, Cambridgeshire, Berkshire and Durham.

17.1 Mathematical tiles. Tenterden, Kent

Mathematical tiles were mainly applied to medium-sized, middle-class, houses in towns; it is rare to find them in villages or the countryside.[1] They were also used on a few of the great houses by ROBERT ADAM, JOHN NASH, JAMES WYATT, JOHN SOANE and HENRY HOLLAND.

The main purpose of the tiles appears to have been a practical means of updating an old building, and in particular a timber-framed house, in order to bring it into line with Georgian taste. In many cases it was only the main façade overlooking the street that was dressed to emulate the fashionable brick-work of the period; side and back walls were left in their original state or clad with weatherboarding or plain hung tiling. Mathematical tiles provided an easy means of masking old openings when new Georgian windows and doors were to be inserted. The tiles also disguised inferior or unfashionable walling materials such as flint, rubble, cob or chalk. During the nineteenth century the tiles were also a practical way of cladding newly erected timber-framed structures.

It has been suggested that mathematical tiles were used as a means of avoiding the 1784 Brick Tax but Mr NORMAN NAIL[2] has shown that this is not so. The tiles were employed from the first quarter of the eigh-

17.2 Mathematical tiles on the wall are battered outwards at the base to align with the face of the brick plinth. The projecting door case masks the edge of the bricks and tiles. Faversham, Kent

17.3 The window frames project to provide a stop for the tiles. Tenterden, Kent

teenth century and were taxed concurrently with bricks in 1784 and at a slightly higher rate than bricks. Tiles were more costly to produce than bricks but the quantity required in a building were likely to have been less than for brickwork and transport may therefore have been cheaper.

The advantages of mathematical tiles as a cladding were that they achieved the appearance of meticulously neat 'brickwork' with fine joints. They were lighter in weight than bricks and were thus more suitable for jettied upper storeys to timber-framed buildings; and it is in this position that they were most frequently used. The tiles were better able than bricks to adjust to movement. Brick nogging panels in a timber-framed building are seldom satisfactory; the weight of the brickwork is too great in relation to the frame and there is the perennial problem of maintaining cracks between frame and panels to prevent the ingress of moisture. Also with a thickness of less than ½ in. (12 mm) 'weather tiles' would have provided a more durable means of protection than a plaster render without significantly increasing the depth of the wall.

Mathematical tiles, says ALEC CLIFTON TAYLOR,[3] 'were intended to deceive, and often did so with great success'. Care was taken in detailing to conceal their true identity. Stops were provided to hide the edges of the tiles; this was achieved by providing a door-case or porch to door openings, and shallow surrounds to windows to allow the frames to be set flush with the external face of the tiles (figures 17.2 and 17.3). A moulded eaves cornice was a satisfactory way of covering the heads of the tiles on the top course. The problem of external angles at the edges of buildings was overcome by bonding the tiles into true brickwork in the return walls, masking the edges of the tiles with brick or white-painted timber quoins or, more commonly,

17.4 Painted mathematical tiles (centre house) Faversham, Kent

concealing the joint with a vertical timber strip. Very occasionally corner tiles were used; these were formed from mathematical tiles with carefully mitred angles made prior to firing or being cut on site.

Most mathematical tiles were sand-faced and the texture often matched that of adjoining brickwork. The dimensions of the face of the tiles followed those of true bricks and they were usually laid in Flemish or header bond.

In the majority of towns 'reds' predominated but 'greys' or 'whites' (which included various shades of yellow), were sometimes employed, particularly in the second half of the Georgian period, when stone-coloured bricks were in favour. Black-glazed tiles were introduced late in the eighteenth century and were used mainly in coastal areas, notably Brighton and Lewes, as an added protection against sea water spray. The black glaze was applied over red tiles.[4] Mr EW O'Shea says that they are lead glazed, 'obtained by applying a paste of galena at the leather stage, to which is added a colouring agent (almost certainly 8 to 10 per cent manganese oxide)'.[5]

17.5 Mathematical tile cladding above a brick gable wall. Faversham

17.6 Repairs to softwood boarding before refixing mathematical tiles

Mathematical tiles were often painted white but it is not known when this custom was adopted. David Duckham[6] has pointed out

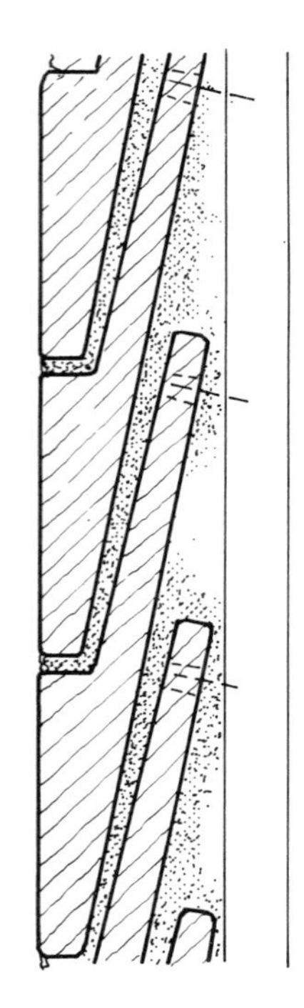

17.7 Section through mathematical tiles showing methods of bedding and fixing to the wall

that painted tiles and glazed tiles can inhibit evaporation and trap water within walls.

Repairs

The choice of backing and the methods of fixing the tiles varied in different areas and also according to individual craftsmen.[7] The usual practice was to attach the tiles to butt-edged softwood boarding that was fixed horizontally, diagonally or vertically to the studding or framing of a timber-framed building. The tiles were bedded in a soft lime/sand mortar and, in most cases, were hung by nails. An alternative method, particularly in the nineteenth century, was to hang or nail the tiles to battens in the manner of roof tiling. Where brick, rubble or flint walls were faced with mathematical tiles the tiles were bedded in a thick coat of lime mortar.

Mathematical tiles have proved durable as a wall covering. Where moisture has penetrated it is usually the timber background or nails that have failed; this is particularly noticeable in lower courses at the base of a wall that is subject to rising damp. Exfoliation of iron nails can crack the tiles around their holes.[8] Spalling of the surfaces of tiles may occur where they are subjected to prolonged damp conditions. Tiles set or pointed in cement mortar will also suffer decay,[9] a strong mortar mix will inhibit evaporation of moisture trapped in the wall.

Slipped tiles or a bulge in a wall may suggest background failure. DAVID DUCKHAM[10] advises against disturbing mathematical tiles unless it is really necessary; there is a risk of loosening the edges of adjoining tiles that are sound and it may not be apparent where to stop. Mr F HADEN[11] warns of the problem of nailing individual tiles where the boarding at the back has become flexible.

Tiles are easy to fix in repair work but the difficulty is in finding suitable replacements; blacks, yellows and creams are seldom available.[12] Second-hand mathematical tiles in Faversham cost 30p each in 1985.[13] A useful source of supply can be the salvage depot of the local authority. New purpose-made tiles can be obtained but they are expensive and they need to be ordered well in advance of work.

Although there was little variation in the dimensions of the exposed faces of mathematical tiles the profiles of the backs varied according to the manufacturers; they were mainly produced in small brickyards within easy reach of the towns in which they were used. Mr B BROWN,[14] a builder at Faversham, believes that the curved-back type, with the ogee profile, preceded the straight-backed variety. He also notes that where blacksmith's hand-made nails were used for fixing, the tiles had square holes. Mr RUSSEL[15] adds that round nails were used in the square holes.

17.8 Repair work at Faversham, Kent. The tiles are bedded in mortar and fixed to horizontal softwood boarding

17.9 Detail from figure 17.8

Early repairs can be recognized by the re-use of iron nails.

Builders now use non-ferrous, small, galvanized nails[16] or stainless steel nails.[17] Aluminium nails are coated with lanolin if applied to treated timber.[18]

Where backing is to be renewed, Mr B BROWN[19] fixes $\frac{1}{2}$ in. (12.5 mm) softwood boarding to the wall. Tile-hanging commences at the base of the wall and each tile in the course is nailed. A weak lime mortar is spread on top of the tiles and the next row of tiles are laid overlapping, bedded in mortar and nailed. If the mortar is too thick it will push the tiles out.[20] DAVID DUCKHAM[21] nails every other course of tiling; for the mortar mix he uses 1 cement:3 lime:12 sand.

Some tiles were never bedded in mortar; they were only pointed. Pointing was essential as a wind barrier. Where wind penetrates it can lift tiles and cause movement to the backing.[22] If rainwater infiltrates through defective pointing between tiles this is seldom a problem as with true brickwork. Mathematical tiles were designed to shed water. However, a hard cement-based pointing mix could inhibit evaporation of moisture.

Mathematical tiles are generally flush pointed. Pointing can be difficult and time

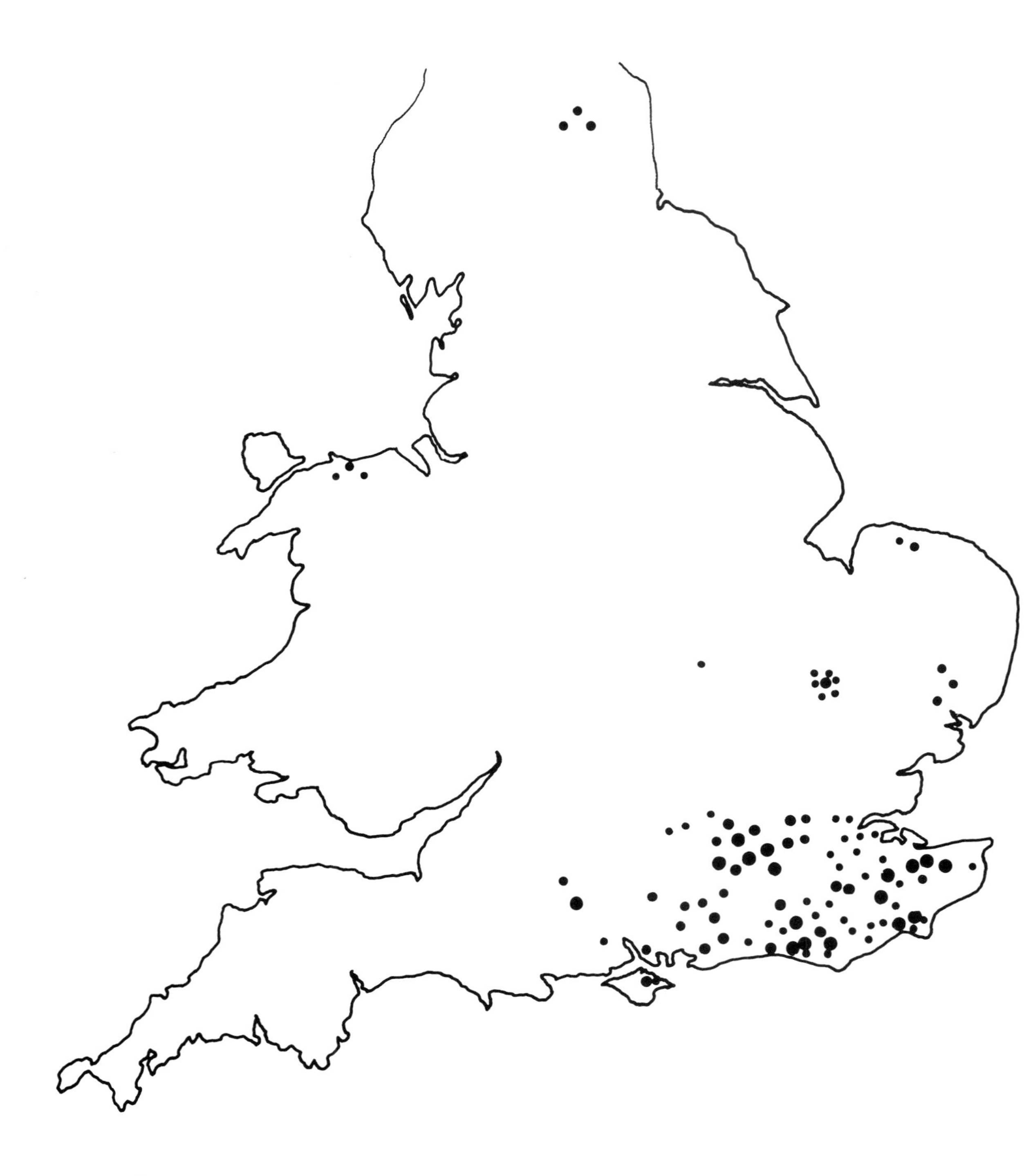

17.10 Distribution of mathematical tiles

consuming where joints are fine. Inserting the pointing mix between greased paper (as with tuck pointing) will help to prevent 'buttering' the edges.

Suppliers of replacement mathematical tiles for repair work

Because of local variations in the shape and colours of mathematical tiles it is always worth investigating local salvage stores (see *Yellow Pages* in local telephone directory). Some county and local councils also maintain salvage depots (contact the Planning Office). A few manufacturers (listed below) are prepared to make special tiles to order. There is, however, usually a long delivery period.

Keymer Handmade Clay Tiles, Nye Road, Burgess Hill, West Sussex RH15 OLZ.
Aldershaw Tiles, Kent Street, Sedlescombe TN33 OSD.
Ockley Brick Co Ltd, Smokeyjacks Brickworks, Wallis Wood, Near Ockley, Surrey.
R Y Ames, 70 Bennerley Road, Battersea, London SW11 6ADS.

ACKNOWLEDGMENT

I wish to express my gratitude for information given by:

MR B BROWN of Faversham, Building craftsman
MR DAVID DUCKHAM, Architect
MR F HADEN of Lewes, Building craftsman
MR NORMAN NAIL
MR I M RUSSEL of Hove, Building craftsman
MR TERENCE PAUL SMITH, Author and lecturer on mathematical tiles.

REFERENCES

1 TERENCE PAUL SMITH, Lecture to the Association for Studies in the Conservation of Historic Buildings
2 NAIL, NORMAN, *Ewell Symposium on Mathematical Tiles* 1981
3 CLIFTON-TAYLOR, ALEC, *The Pattern of English Building*
4 DAVID DUCKHAM, Lecture to the Association for Studies in the Conservation of Historic Buildings
5 E W O'SHEA, Mathematical Tiles: notes of the Ewell Symposium
6 DAVID DUCKHAM
7 I M RUSSEL, Personal communication
8 DAVID DUCKHAM
9 F HADEN, Personal communication
10 DAVID DUCKHAM
11 F HADEN
12 I M RUSSEL
13 B BROWN, Personal communication
14 B BROWN
15 I M RUSSEL
16 F HADEN
17 I M RUSSEL
18 DAVID DUCKHAM
19 B BROWN
20 I M RUSSEL
21 DAVID DUCKHAM
22 I M RUSSEL

FURTHER READING

See *Select bibliography* under '*Mathematical tiles*' page 166.

Part II
ROOFING

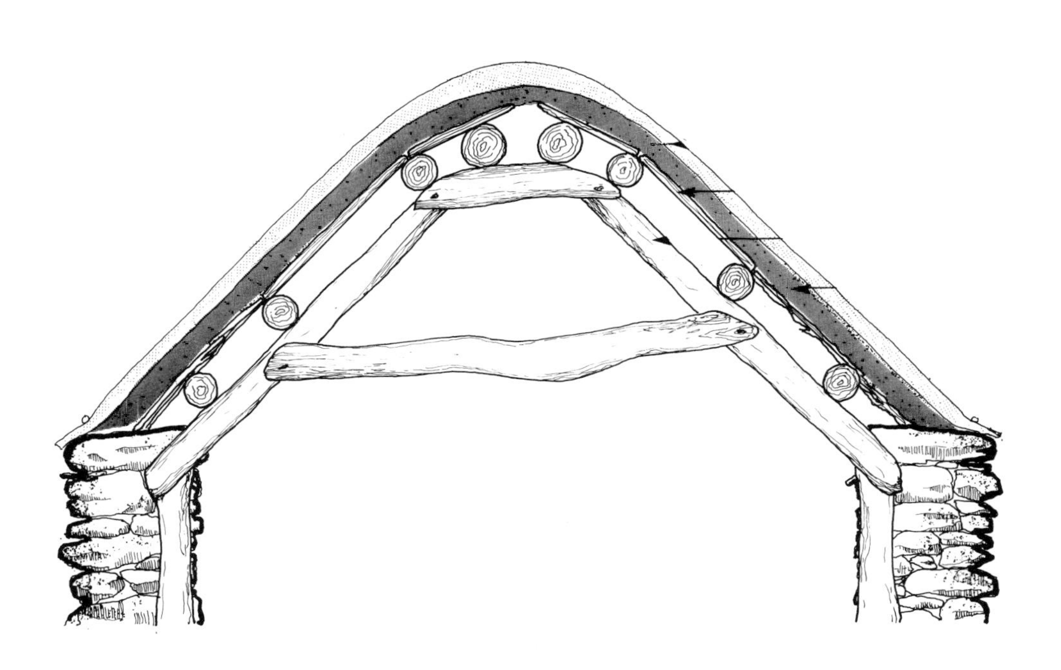

18 HEATHER THATCH IN ENGLAND

18.1 Heather thatch. Bardon Mill, Northumberland in the process of being re-thatched by John Warner of Warwickshire

An eighteenth-century farmhouse, close to the Roman site at Vindolanda in Northumberland, has been bought by the Landmark Trust, and is being carefully repaired using traditional materials and techniques. The roof was originally thatched in heather (or ling, known throughout Northumberland as 'black thatch') over turf sods. Mr John Warner of Warwickshire, with experience in oat straw, rush and turf thatching, as well as heather, is rethatching the building.

The old black thatch of the farmhouse was thought to have been applied around the turn of the century and has been protected by a corrugated iron roof for 60 or more years. Fragments of the old thatch had not completely decayed.

18.2 The old heather thatch has been stripped back to the timbers. Full length and half length oak rafters rest on the purlin and ridge

The old covering was stripped back to the timbers. Most of the original roof structure has survived in good condition and only a few rafters, or sections of rafters, needed to be replaced. The closely spaced cleft oak rafters rest on the ridge, walls and purlins; there are no pegs or nails. The self-weight of the rafters is sufficient to keep them in place. The living accommodation had a plastered ceiling at first floor level. The hayloft, which formed part of the farmhouse, had an open ceiling with the sods exposed to view. These features have been retained.

The original grass sods were square-cut divots arranged overlapping like tiles. Mr Warner has used lengths of lawn turf as sods. These were delivered to the site in long rolls with widths of approximately 24 in. (600 mm). The lawn turf is thinner than the original divots and to increase the thickness the rolls of turf have been laid in two layers; the first set horizontally across the roof and the second vertically. They were placed green side down, without battens, direct to the rafters. There is no fixing at this stage; the weight of the turf is sufficient to keep it in place.

When rain falls on straw or water reed in a thatched roof, movement is along the stalk from one end to the other and any water penetration into the body of the thatch seldom exceeds 2 in. (50 mm). Mr Warner explained that 'heather behaves differently. Water runs down a stem only as far as the first branch, or even to a tiny offshoot, where it is diverted and drips through the thatch. How-

18.3 Rolls of grass sods spread across the rafters

ever, as the thatch is laid in overlapping layers this tends to be mainly at the flowery head as it is the only exposed section on the roof.

'Although rain is easily absorbed by heather thatch some may percolate through to the sods which act as a form of blotting paper and prevent water dripping through to the interior. The open weave of the heather thatch encourages rapid evaporation. However, moisture can sometimes be a problem at the bottom edge of a roof. Drip stones at the head of walls were intended to direct the water away.

'The shorter the heather the finer it is. For thatching it should be 24 to 36 in. [600 to 900 mm] long. If you want long heather this means plants with large branches. Suitable heather is difficult to find; this came from Rothbury near Clinton Wood. Heather grows with the branches spread on the ground, usually to one side, from a central root not of great depth. You take one end and pull it back on itself to rip the root surface together with a hunk of sod which is retained in the thatching process.

'According to the old books "heather was pulled in Spring and kept til the back-end" (autumn), but ideally we would have liked to apply fresh heather because it coarsens when thoroughly dry. The particularly long spell of hot weather at the present has meant that the heather has to be sprayed or soaked prior to use to make it more flexible.

'Heather is laid with root ends facing upwards and the flowery ends downwards. The flowers and leaves will rub off in time as they dry out, which will improve the water run-off. Heather is placed on the roof in chunks, not bundles, and arranged in single overlapping layers with a thickness of 4 or 5 in. [100 or 125 mm] over fixings, and an overall thickness of nearly 24 in. [600 mm]. The 6 in. [150 mm], or so, visible on the exterior at the eaves and gable ends is mis-

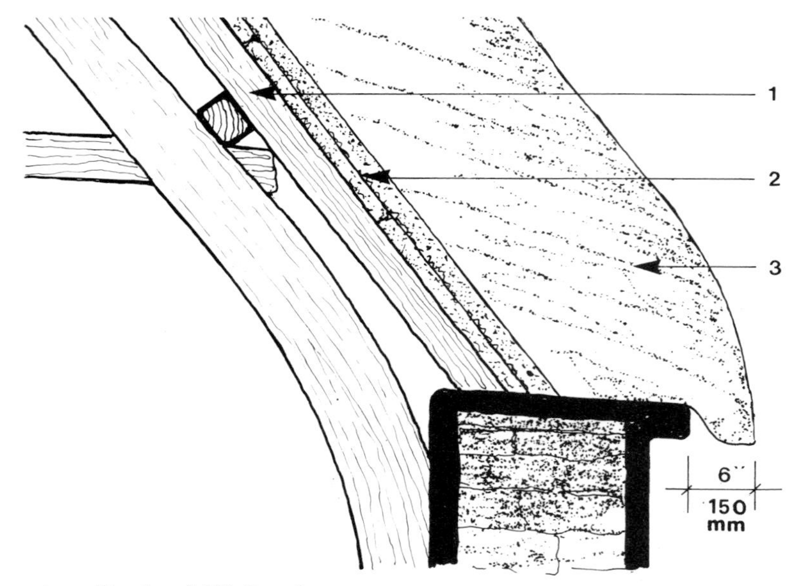

18.4 Heather thatch at Bardon Mill farmhouse
1 Rafters
2 Turf
3 Heather laid in courses

18.5 Detail of the sod underlay to the heather thatching

18.6 Heather is placed on the roof with the sod roots uppermost. Only the flowery ends are visible on the finished thatch

18.7 Gable end of Bardon Mill farmhouse. Only a section of the heather thatch projects above the gable

18.8 A sway, wooden spar and iron hooks to fix the thatch

18.9 Heather over turf sods at Bardon Mill farmhouse

18.10 Old heather thatching, Bowes, Durham. To be re-thatched shortly by William Tegetmeir

18.11 View from the underside of the roof. Bowes

leading as the total thickness is mostly in the roof space [sic: see figure 18.7].

'Each course is held in position with iron sways secured with hooks, or crooks, driven through the turf and into the rafters. No tying is necessary and there are no battens. The surface of the heather is left as thatched and not shaved back; although some books say that the heather was occasionally shaved with an old scythe blade.

'The ridge is formed by bending over alternate handfuls of heather from one side to the other. On top of this we will lay turf, following the pattern of the old thatch, which will hold down the ridge.

'The biggest problem in this part of the country is the wind which can turn back the thatch at the gable ends. In the past there were local people who would patch and re-thatch but we have to ensure a long life for the roof. We will therefore wire-net the whole roof which will also smooth and neaten the final shape of the heather thatch.'

19 THE STOBBING METHOD OF THATCHING

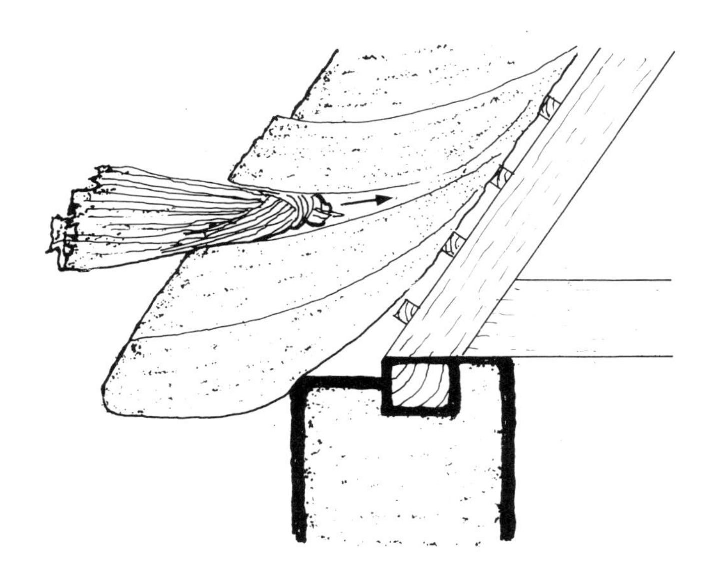

19.1 The knotted end ot the stob is thrust into the old thatch between courses

The usual way of recoating a long straw roof today is to remove all the decayed straw and case over the old thatch with new straw sparred into the old.

Mr WILLIAM TEGETMEIER, a thatcher at York, says that most of the old straw roofs he repairs have been 'stobbed'. It was, he says, 'the commonest form of thatching in Yorkshire and a very good way of doing it. The method was used for both patching and rethatching.

'A handful of straw is knotted at one end; this is known as the *stob*. You simply lift up a layer of the old straw and thrust the knotted end of the stob underneath. This is repeated

19.2 An old 'stob'

19.3 Straw stobbing was also inserted under turf divots

along the course. The old straw above holds the stob in compression. They would stob a whole roof in this way. The old thatch is retained and the new ends of the stobs hang out. The whole surface of the roof is shaved at the end of the job. A fork-headed tool with a handle, about 12 to 18 in. [300 to 450 mm] long, was sometimes used to help insert the stobs.

'A roof was seldom stripped back to the timbers. There was no need to overcoat the old thatch and the method was economical.'

20 THATCH IN SCOTLAND

There are few buildings in the country so evocative of ancient building history as the old stone thatched cottages and barns in parts of Scotland. The simple roofs, with their thin thatch cladding, were constructed by local people who used materials found growing close to the site. Straw, (wheat, rye, barley and oats), was the most widely used type of thatch. Where straw was not readily available alternatives included heather, rushes, bent grass, wild reeds, furze, bracken roots, broom and fir branches.

Some of the old cottages in the Highland islands were without chimneys and smoke from a central hearth found its way out through the thatch. The roof was newly thatched each year as a new crop of straw was harvested and the old thatch, which was well impregnated with soot, formed a valuable fertilizer to spread as a top dressing on potato shoots. With this type of roof no turfs, or sods, were laid beneath the straw.

20.1 The vertically laid thatch at the eaves turns gradually at the gable end to almost the horizontal at the ridge

In other cases, a practice common in low lying areas, the roof was clad with turfs or sods which were protected with only a thin coat of thatch. This method provided good insulation and a durable roof covering.

Most of the roof structures consisted of simple A-frame couples resting on stone wall heads. A tangle of driftwood was roughly levelled and laid on the rafters to form a base for the sods.

When recoating, the thatcher would take a handful of straw, knot the upper ends, and thrust a bunch up under each sod. The thatch was secured with staples, made from twisted hazel twigs, and ropes tied to stones projecting from the wall or by large stones dangling over the edge of the eaves. A course of heather at the eaves acted as a deterrent to birds.

Heather is still used as a main thatching material for houses in some of the higher lying areas of eastern Scotland. Many old churches were once thatched in heather, or heather mixed with other materials. I F GRANT in his book *Highland Folk Ways* says that 'old thatching was made of differently coloured materials arranged in ornamental scallops' and notes that 'its effect was like that of feathers'.

20.2 Thatch over heather sods. Barn at Knockcrome, Jura

20.3 The stone anchors, attached by rope, help to hold down the thatch

Accounts of the durability of heather vary from 20 to 80 years. If bedded in clay this made it firmer and a clay/cow dung slurry applied to the surface bound the thatch more firmly than if held down by a rope.

ALEXANDER (SANDY) BUIE OF KNOCKCROME, *Jura, Scotland* is the fourth generation of Buies to live on the island of Jura and is the last inhabitant of the island to speak Gaelic. He is a farmer and maintains his farm buildings, including the thatched roofs, using the same techniques that have always been used in the area. One of his hobbies is making walking sticks with beautifully carved bone handles in intricate patterns.

SANDY BUIE talked about the buildings of Knockcrome. 'All the houses, barns and byres here were once thatched and they all followed

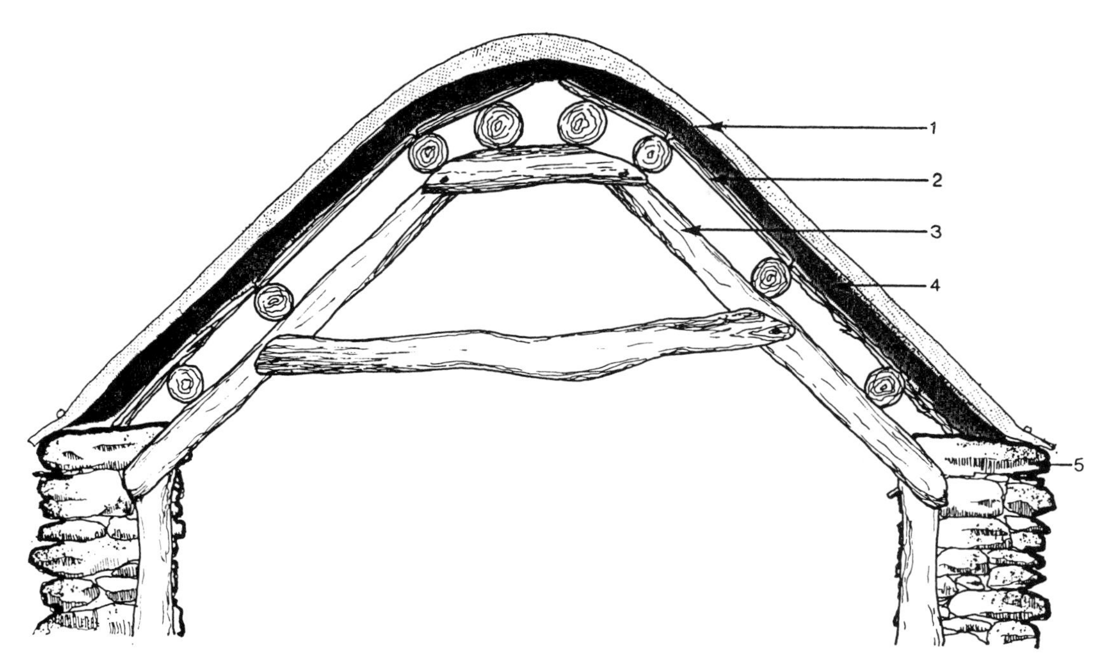

20.4 Section through the interior of a barn
1 Thatch
2 Rafters tied to purlins with heather rope
3 Main couples and ties fixed with wooden pegs
4 Sods placed above willow branches
5 Wall head ledge

the same principle of construction. Most people thatched their own houses; this was unlike many of the other things which we did together, such as helping neighbours to get the corn in while the weather lasted.

'The thatched buildings were very warm in winter and cool in summer. They were also free from condensation; if I wanted to protect my tools I always kept them in a thatched building for in a byre with a corrugated roof they would fall to pieces and the handles would drop off.

Roof construction

'The main couples of a roof were tied with wooden pegs and these pegs would last for nearly a century; nails were used later on. The side timbers (rafters) were tied with heather ropes after which willow branches and sods were laid on top.

'There is plenty of willow on the island and there are two kinds: the tall black willow and the small ground willow and it is this that we use for the roofs. The tips of the bushy branches are placed over the roof timbers; they stay in position and there is no need to tie them. If a row of turf is placed on top of the stone wall the willow branches will press into this which will help to hold them in position. You lay the sods on top of the branches and protect them with 1½ to 2 in. [38 to 50 mm] of thatch; the sods will remain sound for 80 or more years.

20.5 Interior of barn

Sods

'Heather turf is stronger than other turf for the sods; the roots of the heather keep it together. It is the very wee heather growing on rough peaty soil that we use. Turf from rich ground will break up. We lay the turf upside down to its way of growth. We use it in big slabs that are $1\frac{1}{2}$ in. [38 mm] thick. On top of this we put the thatch.

Thatch

'We use a long grass with a bushy head, [a type of rush], that grows here in soft places which we call *thatch* (*tughadh*). You cut it down in September, October and November then put it on the roof at once while it is still green. It takes about half a day to cut 36 sheaves with a scythe, which are tied up into small bundles; this would be enough for a small shed.

'When everyone wanted thatch for their roofs, every available patch was cut down each year and the thatch was always nice and clean. We used to go up to the common grazing ground as there wasn't enough close by. Now we get it from the bottom of our fields and we have to clean the dirt out before using it.

'*Muran* (the Gaelic word for Marram grass) grows on the sea shore but we only have small areas of it in Jura. They use it on the island of Tiree; it has a hard dry stem and is difficult to cut but once you put it on the roof it lasts for a long time.

'To thatch, you start at the bottom and work upwards. The roots of the "thatch" are placed facing towards the ground and the tops are covered with the overlapping layers up to the ridge with a thickness of 1½ to 2 in. [38 to 50 mm]. Two layers are applied to the ridge. If it is done correctly the roof will not leak. No tools are used, only the hands. In some places turf was used on the ridge and the edge of the roof but never on Jura. Sometimes the old folk would put a strip of bulrushes – the type that grows on the shore – at the edge of the roof; thatch was put on top so that the weather would break it and this would last for 50 years.

'As thatch dries you put more on top; you never strip the old thatch. We rethatch houses every second year. We just coat over with about 1½ to 2 in. [38 to 50 mm] on top of the old stuff. You have to extend the thatch 2 to 6 in. [50 to 150 mm] off the edge to stop the water running down the wall.

'Today thatch is secured with wire netting but it used to be done with heather rope. To make the rope you pull up the long heather that grows in moss; it has a very strong stem. You twine it up to form the rope and it will last for two years. The rope is held down with a row of stones at the eaves; no hooks were used, only the stones at the edge. In bad years the thatch would be blown away if not tied down well. A heavy iron bar was also used and this was placed over the netting at the two eaves and tied on the wall with a heavy stone on it.'

20.6 A cottage at the Farming Museum, Auchindrain, Strathclyde

JIM SOUNESS *of Lochgilphead, Scotland* has studied thatched buildings throughout the Scottish Highlands and compiled the *Thatched Buildings Survey of Tiree Coll and Mull* for Argyll and Bute District Council. He is Secretary of Cairdean nan Taighean Tugha (Friends of Thatched Houses) which is an organization that aims to help with the conservation of Highland thatched buildings by ensuring that there is a reliable supply of suitable thatching materials, that traditional skills are retained, and that grant aid is available. He also thatches, and advises on, some of the buildings at the Auchindrain Folk Museum. The museum comprises an ancient 'club farm' that was worked for centuries under the system of communal tenancy; the old stone buildings were built by the people who lived on the farm and they thatched their roofs with material found close to the site.

20.7 Detail showing the sprouting grass sods at the ridge and hips

I am grateful for the following information provided by Mr SOUNESS during a site visit to the Auchindrain Museum.

'In the past, turf was sometimes a building material and roof covering in its own right, but latterly the roof turfs have been covered with thatch. The turf is primarily a bed for the thatch but, if water penetrates, the turf will soak up a certain amount of moisture; this will dry out later due to the ventilation through the open roof timbers and branches upon which it rests.

'The tough, short, grazed heathery turf on the surface of the ground was considered better than the peat turf beneath it. Grassy turf of the area is generally less suitable as the grass might continue to grow on the roof.

'Turfs (Gaelic: *sgròthan*) would commonly be cut in squares or rectangles with sides of about 18 to 24 in. [450 to 600 mm] and with rounded corners. The thickness of each turf might be 2 in. [50 mm] at the centre but tapering towards the edge so that once laid on the roof (with vegetation facing downwards), overlapping in the manner of slates, the upper surface would be fairly level. If the overlaying thatch is properly maintained, the turfs should last a considerable time, at least 50 years, without replacement.

'Stripping off the old thatch would be necessary where turfs were to be replaced, or if the roof had become too heavy, but otherwise a new coating of thatch over the old was normal practice.

'Rushes (Gaelic: *luachair*) are now the normal thatching material at Auchindrain and in much of the Highlands. They are readily available but are one of the poorer materials, sometimes lasting only a year or two before rethatching is needed; however, if thatched skilfully over a sound old thatch they might provide protection for up to 10 years. Rushes are seldom dry enough to ignite which was an advantage over heather, for example, which is highly combustible.

'Heather was generally considered the most durable thatch but involved an immense amount of labour. Bracken also covers acres of ground and was once used as a good and tough thatching material. If pulled by the black-coloured roots (*bun dubh*), the bracken was most durable. It was applied to the roof in overlapping rows with the roots facing downwards and only the roots visible. Bracken that was scythed had a red end (*bun dearg*) and was less durable.' Mr Souness pulled some roots and bent the upper ends to show how a feathered handful would be tucked into the old thatch when repairing the roof. The bracken thatch had an appearance similar to, but less neat than, reed thatch.

'Marram grass (Gaelic: *muran*), a sea grass, also known as *bent grass*, grows in the sand dunes around the coast and is still used as thatch in Tiree and some other islands. It is cut between September and March and can be stored for a few months before use although most thatching takes place in the autumn. Marram grows from 24 to 48 in. [600 to 1219 mm] high; the longer stem is easier to use and provides better protection against the weather. In Tiree, marram is applied to the roof in horizontal rows working up towards the ridge. The first row at the eaves is laid with the marram grass "the right way up" but subsequent rows are laid with the material overlapping and the marram grass in reverse to its way of growth. A new thatch is applied every two or three years which averages about 5 or 6 in. [125 or 150 mm] in thickness; but this varies in different sections of the roof in order to give a rounded, streamlined profile which will provide less resistance to the wind.

'In the past, especially in the islands, thatch would be secured by a tight network of ropes (Gaelic: *sioman*) weighted down with stones. The ropes were hand-made using heather or straw; latterly imported coir yarn was favoured. In parts of the mainland thatch was secured with thin horizontal laths (Gaelic: *lathuis*) at about 18 in. [450 mm] intervals up the roof; these were secured with long pegs made from hazel (Gaelic: *dromanaich*). Nowadays, wire netting tied down and weighted with stones is almost universal.

USEFUL ADDRESS

See page 161 for details of Cairdean Nan Taighean (Friends of the Thatched Houses).

21 STONE ROOFS

Stone slates and stone flags

Limestone and sandstone slates are often referred to as the finest of all roof coverings in Britain. The texture and mellow colours of the roofs in association with the stone walls of churches, colleges, manor houses and simple cottages create a perfect harmony.

Stone roofs today are generally referred to as *stone slates*, *slate stones*, *stone tiles* or *tilestones*. In many localities some of the old names

21.1 Stone slates and flags

1 Roman slates

2 and 3 Examples of old stone slates in the Ryedale Museum, Yorkshire

4 and 5 Cotswold stone 'tiles'

6, 7 and 8 Stones slates and flags from Cumbria

NOT TO SCALE

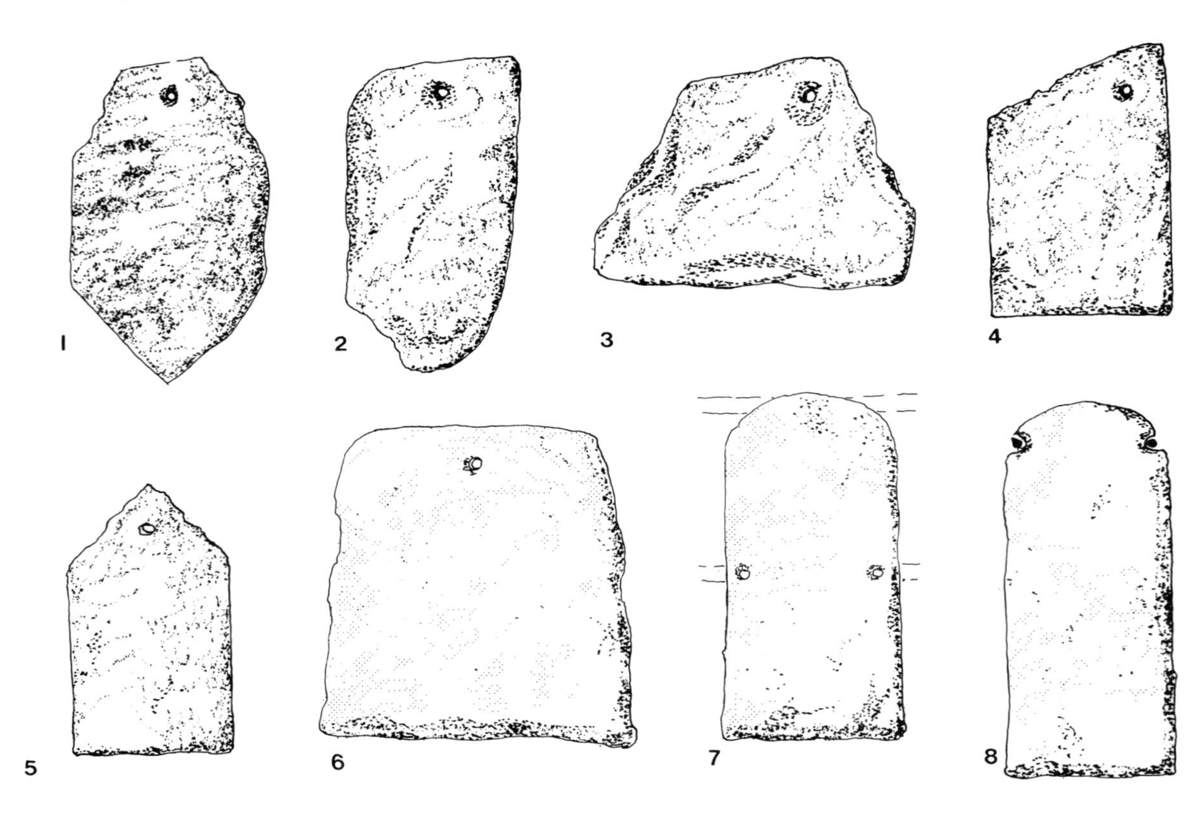

linger on, such as *sclats*, *slats* and *moss stones*. Thick, heavy roofing slabs are known as *flags*, or *flagstones*, and in the Pennines as *thackstones*, *thakstones* or *flatstones*, in Sheffield as *grey slates*, and in Scotland as *brown slates*.

Stone slates are from sedimentary rocks split along lines parallel to the natural bedding plane. The *true slate*, ie Welsh slate, Lake District slate and Cornish slate, differ in that the splitting is along cleavage planes that are at angles to the bedding plane.

Stone clad roofs have been used for centuries in those areas where fissile sedimentary rocks were easily available. Romano-British slates have been found at a number of sites including Chedworth Villa, Gloucestershire. Most of these slates are similar in shape to those generally seen on roofs today; there are also others of oval or hexagonal shape and with a pointed skirt (figure 21.1). The pointed skirt, now uncommon, may well have provided better protection against rain penetration by directing the water to the centre of the slate below.

Records survive on the use and cost of stone roofing from the thirteenth century onwards.[1] From the nineteenth century many of the old stone slates were replaced with the lightweight, more easily worked and therefore cheaper Welsh slates. The old quarries gradually closed down and salvaging stone slates from an outbuilding was often the only source of supply for repair work.

[1] INNOCENT, CF, *English Building Construction*, chapter XII, David and Charles 1971.

True slate

True slate has been used for roofing for centuries in areas close to the quarries but it was only with improved transport that it became widely available throughout the country.

DISTRIBUTION

Stone slates

Limestone

(a) *Cotswold slates* from the sandy beds of the Lower Oolites, cover an area that extends from Gloucestershire and Oxfordshire via Bath to Wiltshire and Somerset. The slates split naturally when still in the ground, as at Filkins Quarry, or were *frosted*, ie kept moist and exposed to the frost to aid delamination, as at Stonesfield. The best known of the old quarries were at Stonesfield, Guiting, Naunton and Eyford. Some suppliers, including quarries still producing stone slates, are listed at the end of this chapter.

Typical sizes of Cotswold slates are from 16 × 24 in. (400 × 600 mm) to 4 × 6 in. (100 × 150 mm) with an average thickness of ½ to 1¼ in. (12 to 30 mm). Approximate weight is 1 tonne per 'square' (100 sq ft – 9.290 square metres). The colour is a pale creamy yellow when first quarried but weathers to warm shades of yellow and brown. These are suitable for roofs of 50 to 60 degrees pitch, with an average of 55 degrees.

(b) *Purbeck stone* slates from the Oolitic limestones of the Isle of Purbeck, Dorset, are the largest and the heaviest of the limestone slates with lengths up to 36 in. (900 mm) and an average thickness of ¾ in. (19 mm). The approximate weight is 1.25 tonnes per square. Colours are shades of greys, blue-greys and browns. Roof pitches are from 40 degrees with an average of 48 degrees.

(c) *Collyweston slates* are from the hard micaceous limestone beds of Northamptonshire, Lincolnshire, Rutland and Cambridgeshire. The best known quarry is at Collyweston, Northants, where the slates are subjected to the frosting process to aid delamination.

21.2 Stone slates at Filkin's Quarry

21.3 Blanchland. Northumberland. An eighteenth-century 'model' village with slate roofs

These slates are more regular in shape, smoother in texture and lighter in weight than Cotswold slates with a fairly constant thickness of $\frac{3}{8}$ in. (9 mm) and an average weight of just over half a tonne per square. Colours are cream and grey. Average pitch of roof is 48 degrees. These slates are bedded in lime mortar unlike other stone slates.

Sandstone

The main sources of sandstone slates or *flags* are the Millstone Grit and Coal Measures of the *Carboniferous System* of the northern counties. The most important are those of the Pennine country, from Derbyshire northwards into Scotland, east Lancashire, north Staffordshire and Yorkshire; also from Bristol northwards through the Welsh Border counties and the West Midlands. The Elland flags of West Yorkshire and the Wensleydale slates from Leyburn formed part of a particularly thriving industry. *Horsham slates* or *Flags*, of the *Cretaceous System* are from the calcareous sandstone beds of the Wealden clay of Surrey, Sussex and Kent.

21.4 Enormous sandstone flags typical of roofs in Blanchland. Known locally as 'grey slates'

Sandstone flags are much larger and heavier than limestone slates, except for the small Ordovician slates quarried at Hoar Edge in Shropshire. Large flags may be up to 36 in. (900 mm) long and 3 in. (75 mm) thick. The surface is smoother in texture than most limestone slates, the flags lie closely together with a generous lap and roof pitches are low, typically 30 to 40 degrees.

True slate

The major sources of true slate, a metamorphosed sedimentary rock, were Scotland, Wales, Cornwall and Cumbria. Some suppliers of slate still in production are listed at the end of this chapter.

(a) *Scotland* The quarries at Ballachulish and Easdale have been the chief sources of supply for centuries. Colours are dark blue from Ballachulish and mid-blue from Easdale.

(b) *Welsh slates* North Wales continues to be the main production area for roofing slate in Britain although now on a much diminished scale. The slate of North Wales can be divided into three geological systems.

First is slate of the early *Cambrian system* in a chain along the north-westerly face of Snowdon from Bethesda to Llanllyfni. This contains the Penrhyn Quarry at Bethesda and the Dinorwic Quarry at Llanberis.

These slates, sometimes referred to as *Bangor slates*, are rugged in texture, hard and durable. Some cottages in the area are still roofed with local slate quarried in the twelfth century.

The second system, of *late Cambrian* or *early Ordovician* origin, includes an area extending from central Snowdon in a south-westerly direction towards Criccieth. These are known as *Caernarvon slates* and were traditionally used in west central and northern areas of Britain as being suitable for severe weather conditions.

The third is the Ordovician system centred on the north-eastern and south-eastern borders of the Harlech Dome. The slate is composed of sedimentary rock without any volcanic ash. The *Portmadoc slates* from the vast subterranean galleries at Ffestiniog and elsewhere, are smoother in texture, softer and thinner than slate from the previously described systems in North Wales.

Colours of the Bangor and Caernarvon slates are blue, blue-purple, grey and occasionally green and grey mottled. Those from the Portmadoc veins are a uniform blue-grey and dark blue-grey. Slates from Vronlog are green.

(c) *Cornwall* The Delabole Quarry near Camelford is amongst the oldest in the country, having been worked continuously since the mid-sixteenth century. The output of slate was at its peak in the mid-nineteenth century. It is also one of the largest with an area of over 40 acres (16.188 ha).

This slate, of the *Devonian System*, is durable, coarse in texture and supplied in standard sizes, in random widths, or random sizes for laying in diminishing courses. The popular small *peggies*, so called because of their method of hanging on battens with oak pegs, range in lengths from 6 to 12 in. (150 to 300 mm) with proportional widths. Colours are grey, weathering to grey-green and rustic red.

A similar, but less durable slate, was produced in Devon. Production ceased at the end of the nineteenth century.

(d) *Cumbria. Westmorland Green Slates*, of the Ordovician System, are mainly from Broughton Moor near Coniston (light green and olive), Spoutcrag (silver and grey-green), Elterwater (pale green), Buttermere (green), Kirkstone Green (light green) and Lakeland Green (olive).

Brathay slate from Ambleside and Burlington slate from Kirby-in-Furness are of the *Silurian System*. Brathay slates are blue-black and Burlington slates blue-grey.

(e) *Leicestershire* Swithland slate comes from the pre-Cambrian rocks of the Charnwood Forest. It was quarried by the Romans and widely used in Leicestershire and parts of Derbyshire and Nottinghamshire until the nineteenth century. The last quarry closed in 1887. The slate is heavy with a thickness of $\frac{1}{2}$ to $\frac{3}{4}$ in. (13 to 19 mm). Colours are mainly blue-grey.

CONSTRUCTION

Cotswold slates

Mr M B Hanks, a builder at Cirencester, has recently re-laid the stone roofs of the nave and chancel of St John the Baptist, a redundant church at Inglesham. He refers to the slates, in this part of Gloucestershire, as *stone tiles* but says that elsewhere, as in Oxfordshire, *stone slates* is the more general term.

The church dates mainly from the thirteenth century but is possibly of Saxon origin. The building has remained essentially unaltered since the sixteenth century and is therefore a rare survival. It was a favourite building of William Morris (founder of the Society for the Protection of Ancient Build-

21.5 The re-slated chancel roof at Inglesham Church, Gloucestershire. New Filkin's stone slates have been mixed with the old

ings). He put his principles into practice and restricted his own repairs to those parts that would extend the life of the church. The same sensitive approach to repairs, in the Society for the Protection of Ancient Buildings tradition, is being carried out today by Mr Hanks.

New Filkin's 'tiles' have been mingled at random amongst the old. The result is a pleasing mélange of rich and mellow colours ranging from pale and golden yellows to various shades of browns. The light yellow Filkin's tiles will weather to deeper shades of yellows and browns in a year or two.

As roofs are stripped and re-slated every hundred years or so, many of the stone tiles are re-used. Mr Hanks says that it is difficult to know the age of them: 'they go from roof to roof. It is the fixings that fail, although tiles can be affected by acids in some towns and those near chimneys may suffer decay through sulphur fumes.

'We prefer to use new stone tiles rather than cut down old tiles. Large old tiles are quite scarce and it is difficult to get hold of them and shape them to size. If you break a large one you have lost a lot of tiles. If you break a small one it doesn't matter so much.

'Mr Aitkin of Filkin's Quarry has only a few days, after quarrying the stone, to cut and hole the tiles. Filkin's tiles cut easily when new and wet but after a week the "sap" dries out and they become hard. Until recently only the bottom of each tile was cut at the quarry but now they are cut on three sides.

'The best tiles have "shoulders", these are the jagged projecting pieces at the top. A hole is put near the top of the longest point but at a

21.6 Filkin's stone slates cut at the base only

21.7 The same stone slates cut on three sides

set distance from the base according to the required size of the tile (figure 21.1). With very big tiles we make two holes. Holes are the size of a peg or nail; $\frac{1}{4}$ in. [6 mm] was usual in old tiles. Years ago we used a little hammer called a pick and we worked both sides of the tile to make the hole. It took a long time as the stone was thick and easy to break. Today we use an electric drill which does not damage the tile and the holes do not show on the finished roof.

'A dressing hammer is used to straighten the sides of the tiles. Part of the work is done by standing the stone on edge and using the side of the dressing hammer to chip off the edges. Dressing forms a drip at the base of each tile to throw off the water. Some modern concrete tiles are set down tight and damp penetration can be a problem.

'As you take off the old tiles you put them on the ground and sort them into sizes. Sorting and dressing takes time; the more time you have the better the roof. Measurements are from hole to base ranging from 6 to 24 in. [150 to 600 mm].

'A double course is placed at the eaves with an overhang. The tiles are graded upwards with the largest at the eaves and the smallest at the ridge. The ridge has to be carefully worked out so that the ridge piece will cover the tiles.'

Widths of the tiles are random. 'The most important thing on these roofs is to have a good side-lap. The size of the side-lap depends on the size of the tile. If you have a 4 in. [100 mm] wide tile, the side-lap will have to come to the centre; it does not matter so much on the top of the roof where the rain run-off is less but at the base of the roof it is important to have an adequate head and side-lap. You push the tiles up as close as possible to make the sides touch.

'The ridge piece on the eastern apex of Inglesham church had to be renewed. This was sawn out of the solid to form a "V" shape, like a miniature roof, and bedded in mortar. The work was done locally at Farmington Quarry near Northleach, figures 21.5 and 21.20 (1).

21.8 New limestone slates at Filkin's Quarry

A slater's rule for measuring tiles is a strip of wood about 1 in. (25 mm) wide and marked at intervals of ½ in. (12 mm). Mr Hanks has some antique stone slaters' rules with Roman numerals. 'We continue to use imperial measurements for this work. We transfer marks from the rule to a stick or lath; this covers most tiles from 6 to 24 in. [150 to 600 mm]. Often we measure in half inches [12 mm]. We usually start at 6, 6½, 7, 7½ up to 12 in., then we go 12, 13 and 14 in.

'At one time I employed a slater who worked in the old way. He put tiles with an odd number of inches on one side of the roof and an even number on the other. Most of the old stone tiles we take off a roof are like that; it must have been the way it was done a hundred or more years ago. On the north slope they were 24, 22, 20, 18, 16; on the other side they were 23, 21, 19, 17. Always in 2 in. [50 mm] spacings. I am not convinced that it was always a good system. You can't get the graduations to look right unless the lap is varied. Today we have to be careful with the lap and gauge because of the scarcity of tiles; you calculate more carefully and try to avoid having too many rows of tiles.

'Most of the roof coverings we take off are about 100 years old. The laths decay first and then the pegs. We use sawn laths in repair work; riven laths are probably stronger but we are not able to get them in this part of the world.

'We use stainless steel nails, usually serrated with large heads and of various lengths. We still use wooden pegs, in some repair work, which we make ourselves usually of riven oak, of a size to fit tightly into a round hole.

'Torching is expensive in labour; it takes longer to torch than to put tiles on. We felted the chancel roof at Inglesham; torching was not possible as it would have meant disturbing

21.9 Old limestone slates on the porch at Inglesham Church

21.10 Eaves detail of the porch. Inglesham Church

the fine old boarding of the chancel ceiling.

'There is not much of a problem with moss or lichen although it can be thick on the north sides of some roofs. I have never found that it made much difference to a roof. Sometimes a customer prefers the appearance of a "clean" roof and we are asked to scrape it, when we also replace loose tiles or other repairs. Some of the clinging moss is difficult to remove but the lumps come off easily. We do not use fungicides; they brighten the tiles and we have our doubts as to whether the chemicals are good for the stone.

'Until about 20 years ago our work on stone roofs was scrape and repair but as labour costs rose this was no longer required by the farm estates. All the estates used to have it done regularly every year; the old roofs then lasted about twice as long. Old roofs today tend to be renewed rather than repaired.'

Stone and slate roofs of the Lake District

I am grateful to Mr RAVEN FRANKLAND for providing most of the information in this section (pages 144–148).

Westmorland green slate was first introduced into Ravenstonedale in 1664. The high pitched roofs of some of the older buildings show that they were thatched. No traces remain of the type of thatching material used, although one field at Ravenstonedale is known to have been set apart for growing reeds specifically for thatch. A layer of stone flags at the top of a wall, to throw off the rain, was used for a thatched roof as well as for a stone slated roof.

Many of the steeply pitched roofs were

21.11 A heavy sandstone flagged roof, at Ravonstonedale, Cumbria, slated by Mr Raven Frankland in 1960. The two lower courses of stone lie flat together. (Figure 21.14 shows a tilt between the two lower courses. Both methods are satisfactory)

21.12 A sixteenth-century cottage in Ravonstonedale, Cumbria. The original high-pitched roof, to a single storied building, was raised in the eighteenth century to accommodate a second storey and stone slates replaced the old thatch. It was a humble building and therefore not considered worthy of 'green slates'

21.13 Sedbergh, Cumbria

adapted to a shallow pitch more suited to heavy stone flags (known locally as *grey slate*), with a wide lap. Occasionally the old cruck frames have been retained in situ with a new roof structure inserted above. Often an indication of this on the exterior of a building is a wall that has been raised to accommodate the change.

Westmorland green slate was considered superior to grey sandstone flags and was used progressively on the 'smarter' buildings from the mid-seventeenth century onwards. It had always been used, apart from thatch, near the quarries. As demand grew it was taken further afield by horse (itself a difficult means of transport) up to the railway era.

Green slate was sometimes applied only to the front facing roof slope of the main façade and the old stone flags were retained else-

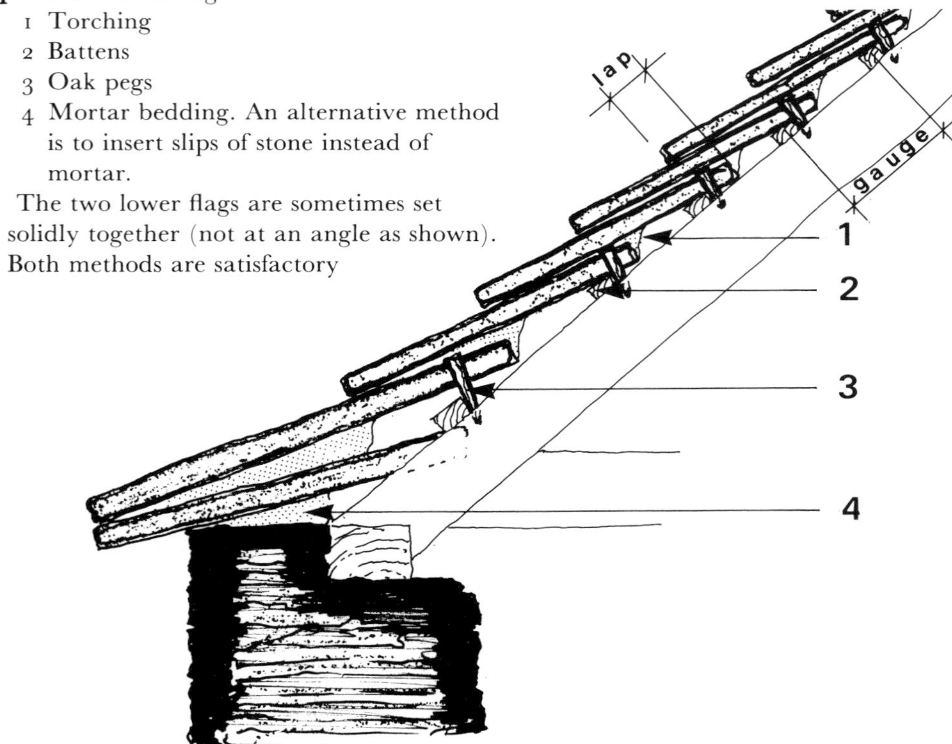

21.14 Sandstone slating
1 Torching
2 Battens
3 Oak pegs
4 Mortar bedding. An alternative method is to insert slips of stone instead of mortar.

The two lower flags are sometimes set solidly together (not at an angle as shown). Both methods are satisfactory

21.15 Blanchland, Northumberland

21.16 An old privy in a garden at Blanchland. The heavy sandstone flags were hung on fragile battens with oak pegs. The battens were nailed to heavy oak joists

where on the house, its outbuildings and barns.

The Westmorland green slate from Elterwater in the Langdale Valley is among the best in the world being produced today. It is hard, dense and almost indestructible. The granular structure of the roofing slates allows just enough air to circulate between laps and this helps moisture to evaporate. Slates of many old roofs close to the quarry are still sound after 300 years.

Slates are dressed on the underside by striking the edge of the skirt, with a slater's hammer, to form a sharp bevel edge intended to throw off the water. Holes are made with a sharp pointers slater's pick, also on the reverse side of the slate.

When reslating an old roof it is best, from the conservation point of view, to reuse the old stone slates, now difficult to obtain, from the eaves upwards and finish off towards the ridge with Westmorland slates.

21.17 Westmorland slates laid in courses of diminishing sizes from eaves to ridge. The Lake District

Westmorland green slate

Westmorland green slates are laid in carefully graded courses with the largest and thickest slates at the eaves and sizes diminishing to the small *peggies* approximately 6 in. (150 mm) long at the ridge. Widths of slates are random and range from 40 in. (1000 mm) at the base of the roof to 6 in. (150 mm) at the top. The diminuation of the courses is not always regular. For instance, there may be two courses laid to an 8 in. (200 mm) gauge, (the gauge is related to the uniform lengths of slates in a row), and perhaps three courses laid to a 7 in. (175 mm) gauge.

Most slates are head-nailed, or head-hung (see figure 21.1), following the traditional practice, by fixing with a riven oak peg driven tightly into a hole at the head of a slate. Head-hung or head-nailed slates provide good protection against rainwater as there are at least two thicknesses of slate above each hole. But the slates, particularly in positions of extreme exposure, may twist or can be lifted by strong winds. Snow and rain may be driven into the roof and the movement can damage the holes of the slates. Shoulder-fixed slates, with a pair of holes at a level lower than head-fixed nails, are held tighter and there is less movement; but they take longer to fix; they are also more difficult to repair and to gauge.

In exposed locations large slabs are also placed at gable ends to withstand the vicious Lake District winds. Another safeguard was to build up the gable walls parallel to and at a higher level than the roof slope to form a parapet.

These Lakeland roofs generally need reslating every 70 to 100 years. Much depends upon the quality of the slate. It is always the battens and fixings that deteriorate first. Even with modern nails reslating may be necessary after 100 years.

In repair work some slates will require no more than a scrape down but others will need to be re-dressed and, if damaged, reduced in size in order to be set in a higher course.

The mean length of a slate is measured from hole to base. The length above the hole may be 3 in. (75 mm) or more. The lap remains constant throughout all courses, although this rule may be broken and the lap gradually reduced for the small *peggies* at the ridge. It is the gauge that decreases upwards. The side-lap or 'bond' is a minimum of 3 in. (75 mm).

Torching, known locally as *tearing* or *tiering*, is composed of a good lime mortar in proportions of 1 lime:2 to 2½ sand and plenty of hair. It is gently but firmly pressed into the gap at the backs and undersides of the slates. This helps to prevent snow being blown into the roof space. Tearing, in preference to roof felting, is applied to many old buildings in the area.

Some Lakeland roofs have a slight 'dish' or 'break'. The appearance is that of an old roof with rafters bowing under strain. But the dish is intentional and has been carefully designed by the carpenter. The inclination helps the lower edges of the slates to sit more closely together with the tail of each slate tight up against the one below which gives additional protection against driving rain. A tilting fillet provides an uplift to the double eaves course which will help to throw water well clear of the wall; this is a necessary adjunct to a roof without a gutter.

The construction of the roof is standard with ridge, purlins and wall plate. The dip is typically 2 in. (50 mm) at midpoint over a

21.18 The gentle 'dish' or dip in the roof is just apparent in this Lake District barn

21.19 Westmorland slates with interlocking slates at the ridge known as *wrestlers*

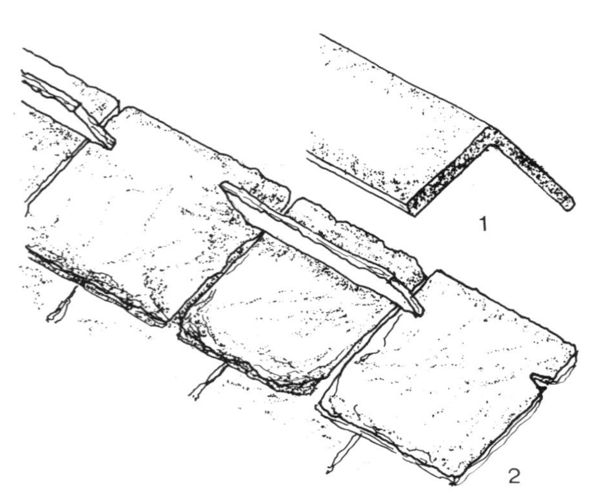

21.20 Ridge details
1 Sawn sandstone ridge in random lengths from 24 in. (600 mm) long
2 Interlocking *wrestlers*

span of 12 ft (3.65 m) between ridge and eaves. The dish is made by dropping the middle purlin to a lower level than the other purlins. In some of the old buildings small trees were split in half and used as spars. The heartface of the timbers were placed facing the inside of the roof which increased their flexibility. This was the reverse to traditional building practice where the heartface is set to the exterior.

Roof timbers today are generally of sawn softwood or riven oak. They are cleft by hand or by machine. With the latter results are similar but the process is speedier and safer than by hand.

Ridges are formed from pieces of solid sandstone, usually from the west coast of Cumbria, and chiselled to a 'V' shape (see figure 21.20 (1)) in random lengths typically from 24 to 48 in. (610 to 1220 mm) and

21.21 Eaves detail of a Lake District barn. The wall plate is bedded on turf in the traditional manner. The turf provides a level underlay to the plate and also provides protection from the sharp edges of the random stone in the walls

21.22 A slate holing machine, clamped to a plank, used on Westmorland slates

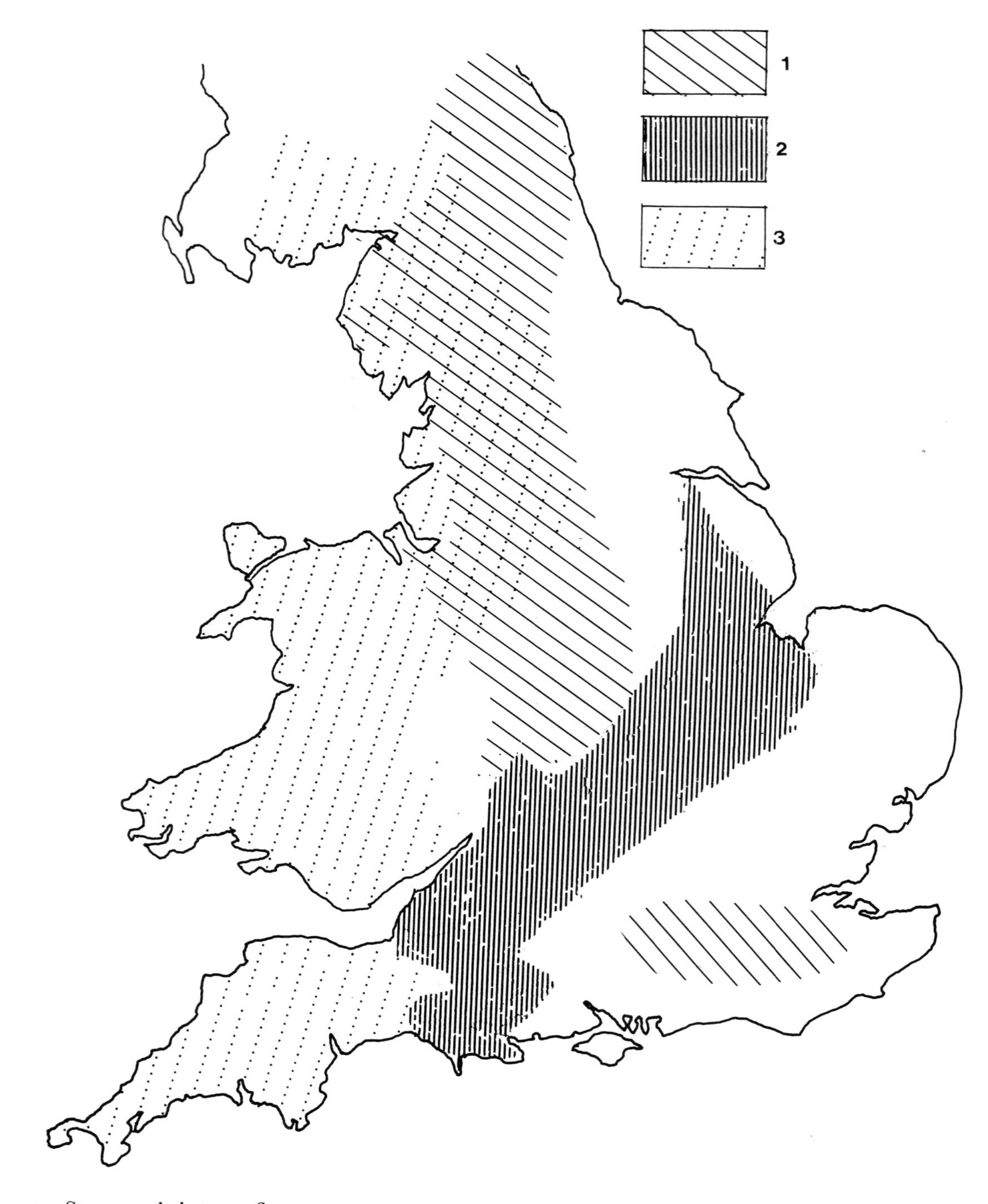

21.23 Stone and slate roofing
1 Sandstone flags
2 Limestone slates
3 True slates

bedded in lime mortar. An alternative ridge is formed from pairs of *wrestler* slates (sometimes known as *dogs and bitches*). Slots are cut at the heads of the slates which interlock to form a 'V' joint which is filled with lime mortar as the ridge is fixed into position.

USEFUL ADDRESSES

Collyweston Stone Slaters Trust
61 High Street, St Martins, Stamford, Lincolnshire. Promotes research into the production and use of these slates and publishes information on methods of use.

Men of the Stones
The Rutlands, Tinwell, Stamford, Lincolnshire PE9 3UD. Gives advice on the conservation of stonework and the selection and use of stone.

North Wales Slate Quarries Association
Bryn Llanllechid, Bangor, Gwynedd, LL57 3LG.

QUARRIES AND SUPPLIERS OF STONE SLATE AND SLATE

STONE SLATES – SANDSTONE

Bolton Woods Quarried at Bolton Woods, Bradford. *Enquiries:* Percy Pickard Ltd, Fagley Lane, Eccleshill, Bradford, Yorkshire.

Caithness Flagstone Quarried at Spittal Quarry, by Halkirk, Caithness.
Owners: A and D Sutherland Ltd, 69 Princes Street, Thurso, Caithness.

Kerridge (Macclesfield stone). Quarried at Bridge Quarry, Windmill Lane, Nr Macclesfield, Cheshire.
Owners: Macclesfield Stone Quarries Ltd, 2 Robin Hill, Biddulph Moor, Stoke on Trent, Staffordshire.

Liscannor Quarried at Doolin, Co Clare, Ireland. *Owners:* North Clare Quarry Ltd, Doolin, Co Clare.

Shipley Quarried at Shipley Quarry, Marwood, Barnard Castle, Egglestone. *Owners:* TH Cross, Rose Cottage, Lartington, Barnard Castle, Co Durham.

STONE SLATES – LIMESTONE

Collyweston Quarried at Collyweston, Nr Peterborough, Northamptonshire.
Owners: Bullimores Sand and Gravel Ltd, South Witham, Grantham, Lincolnshire.

Filkin's Quarried at Filkin's, between Burford and Lechlade. *Owners:* Filkin's Quarries Ltd, Brook House, Cricklade, Wiltshire, SN6 6DD.

TRUE SLATE

Burlington Blue Grey, Moss Rigg, Broughton Moor, Spoutcrag, Elterwater, Brandy Cragg *Quarries:* Burlington at Kirkby-in-Furness, Cumbria. Broughton Moor near Coniston. Elterwater and Spoutcrag in the Langdale Valley, Lakeland Green from Bursting Stone Quarry, Coniston Old Man and from Moss Rigg Quarry, Tilberthwaite, Coniston, Brandy Cragg Quarry, Coppermines Valley, Coniston.
Owners: Burlington Slate Ltd, Kirkby-in-Furness, Cumbria LA7 7UN.

Buttermere Quarried at Honister Quarry. *Operators:* Buttermere and Westmorland Green Slate Co Ltd, Honister Mines and Quarries, Borrowdale, Nr Keswick, Cumbria CA12 5XN.
Owners: Penrhyn Quarries Ltd, Bethesda, Bangor, Gwynedd LL57 4YG.

Delabole Quarried at Delabole, North Cornwall. *Owners:* Delabole Slate Ltd, Pengelly House, Delabole, Cornwall PL33 9AZ.

Gloddfa Ganol Quarried at the Gloddfa Ganol and Ffestiniog slate quarries.

Owners: Ffestiniog Slate Quarry Ltd, Gloddfa Ganol Slate Mine,
Blaenau Ffestiniog, Gwynedd LL41 3NB.
Kirkstone Green Quarried at the summit of the Kirkstone Pass, Ambleside.
Owners: Kirkstone Green Slate Quarries Ltd, Skelwith Bridge, Ambleside, Cumbria LA22 9NN.
Welsh Slate Quarried at Blaenau, Ffestiniog-Maentwrog Road.
Owners: B Kavanagh & Sons, 7 Mills Row, Blaenau Ffestiniog, Gwynedd.

The above list is summarized from information given in the *Natural Stone Directory*, 7th edition 1987. By permission of the publishers, Stone Industries, Ealing Publications Ltd, Weir Bank, Bray, Maidenhead, Surrey SL6 2ED.

PUBLICATIONS

British Standards

BS 680 *Roofing slates* – Part 1 *Imperial units*, Part 2 *Metric units*.

BS 5534 *Code of Practice for Slating and Tiling* (Part 1 *Design*).

22 OAK SHINGLES

Shingles were a common form of roof covering for all types of buildings – cathedrals, castles, churches and cottages – throughout the Middle Ages. Before this they were used by the Romans and later continued in general use for lesser buildings until the eighteenth century. These wood tiles are still seen on ecclesiastical buildings in the southern, south eastern and eastern counties together with a few isolated examples in other parts of the country.

Shingles may be riven or they may be sawn. Those that are cleft are more pleasing in texture, and are more durable, than those that are sawn. Splitting oak along the grain avoids disrupting the fibres and as rain falls on the roof it is channelled along the grain in a similar manner to water on thatch. Slicing across the grain, as may happen in the sawing process, will reduce the strength and can lead to curling and splitting.

Cleft oak shingles have been virtually unobtainable in England for many years. Cedar shingles are imported for domestic buildings but cleft oak shingles, if properly made and carefully laid, will last more than twice as long, with a life span of 80 to 100 years.

22.1 St Peter's church, Newdigate, Surrey

St Peter's church in the Wealden village of Newdigate, Surrey, dates from the thirteenth century. The walls are of roughly coursed random stone and the main roof is of Horsham stone slabs. The tower at the west end of the church is of particular interest. The spire and the roof, midway down the tower, are clad in cleft English oak shingles. The walls of

22.2 St Peter's church, Newdigate, Surrey

the tower are weatherboarded. The height to the top of the spire is 60 ft (18.28 m).

A message in the lead ball at the apex stated that the last reshingling had been completed in 1912. (It is traditional for steeplejacks to leave a message thus, for posterity.)

Mr Roger Sawtell, who was Church Warden, was closely involved in the decision on how to reshingle the roof of the tower and the spire, and also in making the shingles. I am grateful for the following information from him on how the work was carried out.

In 1977 the shingles showed signs of curling and slipping; this was thought to have been connected with the hot summer, which was followed by winter gales, in the previous year. East and Company, a firm of steeplejacks in Essex, had a small stock of oak shingles sufficient for immediate repair work but warned that a complete reshingling would be necessary within five years. The architect, Mr Bevil Greefield, and the Parochial Church Council were reluctant to accept the advice that cedarwood shingles should be used as a substitute. The smooth mechanical texture of cedarwood shingles, the colour and the longevity of cedar in relation to oak made the proposal unattractive. Sweet chestnut was considered but rejected because such shingles are thicker and their weight would have increased the load on the spire. St Peter's is an essentially oak and stone church and oak was the material chosen for the new shingles.

In 1979, after a year long search, Roger Sawtell tracked down Ernie Harris, a

22.3 Oak shingles on the lower roof of the tower

retired shingle maker, who lived in Leicestershire where he demonstrated his craft. Two brothers, PAUL and ANDY WRIGHT, who had been cleaving timber for many years, as part of their woodland craft on an estate close to Newdigate, agreed to help.

ROGER SAWTELL and one of the WRIGHT brothers decided to do a feasibility study. They felled a tree, cut it into logs and made some shingles.

22.4 Section through trunk of a tree with a girth greater than 6 ft (1.8 m)
1 Shingles
2 Sapwood
3 4 in. (1016 mm)
4 Bark

As the craft of shingle-making was close to extinction Mr HARRIS accepted an invitation to stay in Newdigate for about a week where he passed on his skills and some of his tools and other equipment to ROGER SAWTELL and the WRIGHT brothers.

Twelve oak trees of varying sizes were donated to the church by local people. Many more were offered but most proved to be unsuitable. This was due to twisting in the stem; it was possible to test whether the grain was straight by removing a small section of bark.

Cleaving and shaping the shingles is most easily done within two months of felling the tree whilst the wood is still green.

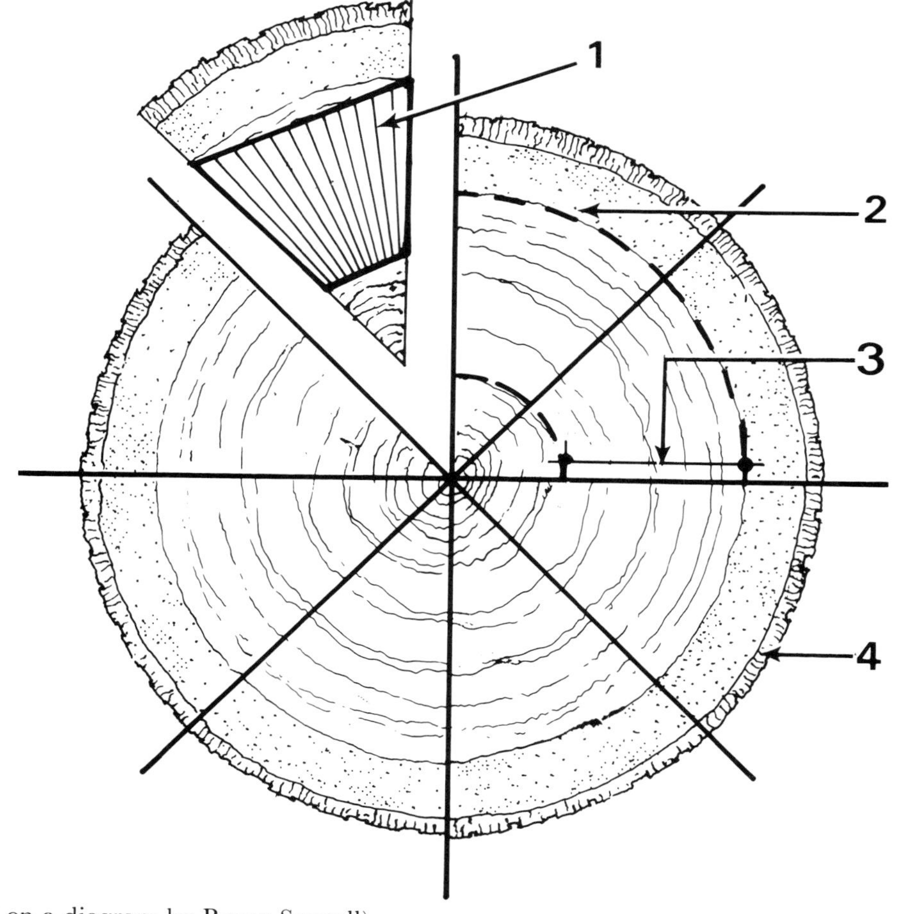

(Based on a diagram by Roger Sawtell)

'The art of cleaving shingles from oak', says Mr Sawtell, 'is that the cleaver follows the grain of the wood and does not cut across the fibres as with a saw. Following the grain gives the shingles a stable and waterproof quality. With oak this means splitting on the radius. The tree must have at least a two metre girth and have a straight branch-free stem. Logs, the length of a shingle 12 in. (300 mm), are split into eight "cheese"-like sections. The curved sapwood and the centre point are cleaved off. The remaining block is only roughly square but the cleaver is able to divide it, always splitting in the middle to equalize the pressure.'

Oak is relatively easy to split evenly but as each piece gets thinner it becomes more difficult to hold and a *brake* is used as a clamp. The three basic tools used in shingle making are the cleaver used for splitting the oak, the axe and the draw knife. Ernie Harris gave the Wright brothers a special axe the blade of which is cut rather like a chisel; one side is flat and the other side has a chamfer. The axe is used to do the rough trimming and will remove any lumps. The rest of the trimming or smoothing is done with the draw knife while the craftsman is seated at the bench. The mallets are traditionally made from a lump of holly; this is a dense wood with branches growing at right angles to the stem which can be used to form the handle of a mallet.

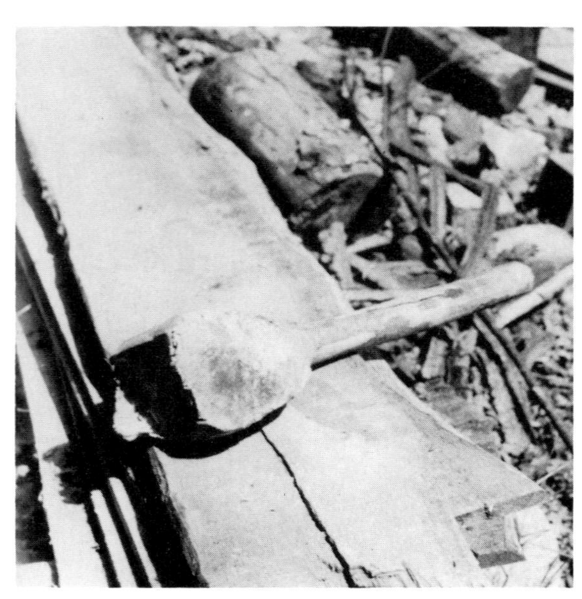

22.5 A mallet of holly wood

A *brake* is an arrangement of poles designed to hold the oak firmly during the splitting process; the piece is pushed, bit by bit, into the brake as it is cleaved. The Wright brothers often used the stump of a tree for the same purpose; they pushed the oak into a cleft that they had cut in the stump and used leverage on the handle of the cleaver to split the oak apart.

Peter Harknett, the steeplejack who eventually fixed the tiles, gave valuable advice on the production of the shingles. He had rejected a few of the first shingles made during the feasibility study; he said that too much trouble had been taken in making them and they were too smooth. Capillary action can arise if shingles are laid overlapping without an airspace between. Shingles thereafter were made smooth on only one side.

As shingles tend to dry out quickly it may be necessary to cover them with damp sacks or sawdust to slow down the process if they are to be stored.

The spire of St Peter's church is diagonally boarded in pitch pine. The horizontal boarding on the exterior face was only discovered when some of the old shingles were removed. Both layers of boarding were retained and treated with preservative. The new shingles were fixed direct to the horizontal boarding without battens. An underfelt was not used as it would have restricted ventilation. Lead flashings were fixed in vulnerable areas.

Peter Harknett and his two young assistants did much of the work hanging from 'bosuns' chairs'. Scaffolding, which was sup-

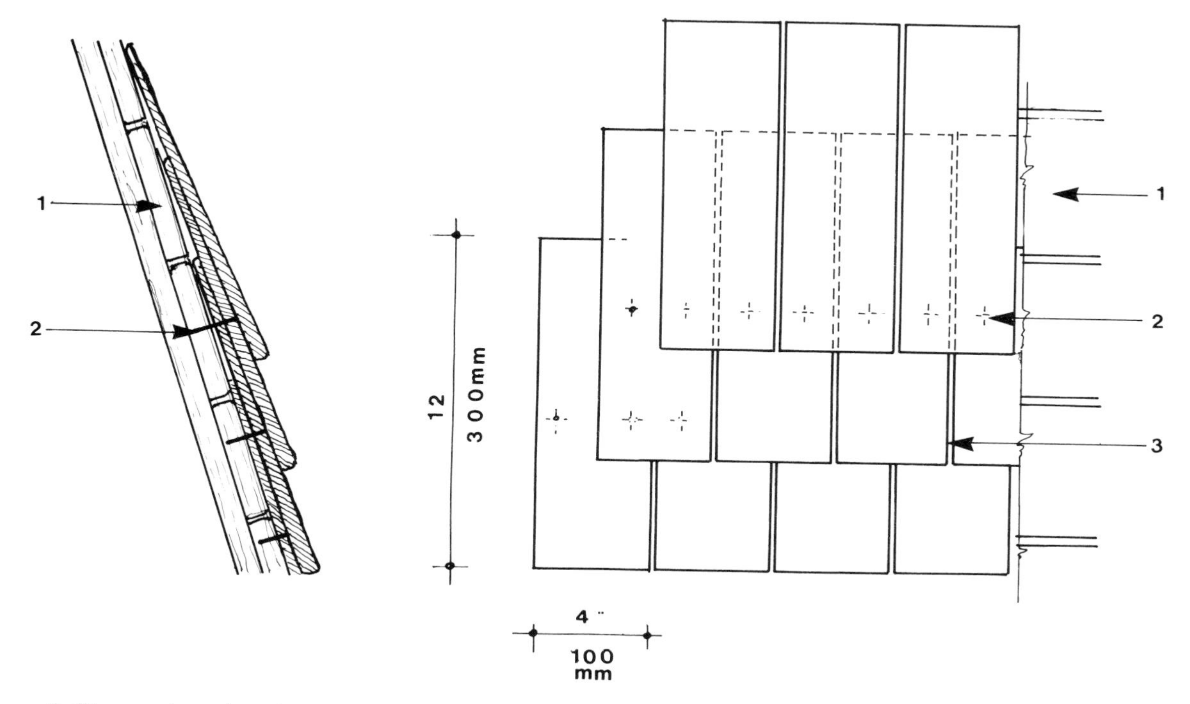

22.6 Plan and section showing fixing of shingles
1 Square edged boarding
2 Each shingle is twice nailed to boarding with annular ring-shanked stainless steel nails
3 $\frac{1}{8}$ to $\frac{1}{4}$ in. (3 to 6 mm) clearance between shingles

ported on heavy duty brackets, was only necessary for the upper half of the spire.

A steeplejack's tools are kept to a minimum. Mr HARKNETT used a multi-purpose tool that resembled a fireman's axe in appearance; it can be used to extract nails, chop and cut, and can also act as a gauge. The old shingles remained in place and were only removed in sections just before the new ones were ready to be applied. The shingles were laid overlapping with each one twice nailed to the square-edged boarding. They were fixed with annular ring-shanked nails of stainless steel to prevent withdrawal. Holes were bored in shingles where there was a danger of splitting the oak or fixing was difficult.

22.7 Fixing the shingles

Detailing at the hips had originally consisted of single courses of butt-jointed shingles. PETER HARKNETT considered this the weakest point in the old shingling and said that if it was repeated in the new work it would be the first area to deteriorate. Boards were inserted in the triangular recesses at the hips with the top of the boarding level with the outer face of the shingles. New shingles were then applied over the boards which gave added protection.

PETER HARKNETT placed a message, which gave a description of the newly completed work, in the lead finial at the apex of the spire. He said 'it must be unique in the country for a church spire to be clad in shingles made in a village by village craftsmen from village oak trees; this wouldn't have happened for ages and ages. It goes back to feudal times and may never happen again'.

USEFUL ADDRESSES

The Ancient Monuments Society
St Andrew-by-the-Wardrobe, Queen Victoria Street, London EC4V 5DE. *Secretary:* Matthew Saunders. Concerned with the study and conservation of ancient monuments and historic buildings of all ages. Publishes Transactions annually; sections of which are available as reprints

The Ancient Monuments Board for Scotland
The Scottish Development Department, 17 Atholl Crescent, Edinburgh EH3 8JN

The Ancient Monuments Board for Wales
Welsh Office, Cathays Park, Cardiff CF1 3NQ

The Architectural Association
34–36 Bedford Square, London WC1 3EF. Post-graduate course in Building Conservation: thesis may be seen in the library. Triangle Bookshop in basement

ASCHB (Association for Studies in the Conservation of Historic Buildings)
Hon Secretary: Mrs Margaret Davies, 20a Hartington Road, London W4 3UA. Organizes lectures and visits for members. Publishes Transactions annually

Avoncroft Museum of Buildings
Stoke Prior, Bromsgrove, Worcestershire

British Association for Local History
45 Bedford Square, London WC1B 3DP. *Secretary:* Bettie Miller. Organizes courses. Information service and publications

British Museum
Conservation Department, Great Russell Street, WC1B 3DG

British Trust for Conservation Volunteers
36 St Mary's Street, Wallingford, Oxfordshire OX10 0EU. Organizes conservation working holidays, publications

The Building Centre
26 Store Street, London WC1E 7BT. Bookshop and building material exhibits

The Building Conservation Trust
Apartment 39, Hampton Court Palace, East Molesey, Surrey KT8 9BS. *Director:* John Griffiths. Maintains a large permanent exhibition and organizes temporary exhibitions on methods of repair to buildings of all ages

Building Research Establishment
Garston, Watford WD2 7JR. Publications and advice on technical matters

Cairdean Nan Taighean Tugha (Friends of the Thatched Houses)
Secretary: Jim Souness, 6 Fernoch Drive, Lochgilphead, Argyll PA31 8PZ. Helps to retain traditional thatched buildings in Scotland. Obtains maintenance grants, ensures supplies of thatching materials. Encourages the passing on of relevant skills. Publishes annual Newsletter

Civic Trust
17 Carlton House Terrace, London SW1Y 5AW. The Trust maintains a register and supports and advises local amenity societies throughout Britain. Publishes *Heritage Outlook*.
North-West Trust, 69 Rodney Street, Liverpool L1 9EX.
North-East Trust, 34–35 Saddler Street, Durham DH1 3NU

Civic Trust for Scotland
24 George Square, Glasgow G2 1EF

Civic Trust for Wales
46 Cardiff Road, Llandaff, Cardiff CF5 2DT

The Clay Roofing Tile Association
Federation House, Station Road, Stoke-on-Trent ST4 2TJ

Collweston Slaters Trust
61 High Street, St Martins, Stamford, Lincolnshire

Conservation Bureau
Rosebery House, Haymarket Terrace, Edinburgh EH2 5EZ

Council for British Archaeology
7 Marylebone Road, London NW1. Serves as a national information centre on all aspects of British Archaeology

Council for the Protection of Rural England (CPRE)
4 Hobart Place, London SW1W 0HY. *Director:* Robin Grove-White

Council for the Protection of Rural Wales
32 High Street, Welshpool, Powys. *Director:* SRJ Meade

CoSIRA (Council for Small Industries in Rural Areas)
See *Rural Development Commission*

Countryside Commission
Head Office: John Dower House, Crescent Place, Cheltenham, Gloucestershire GL50 3RA. Publish useful background material on many aspects of rural conservation

Countryside Commission for Scotland
Battleby, Redgorton, Perth PH1 3EW

Countryside Commission (Wales)
8 Broad Street, Newtown, Powys SY16 2LU

Crafts Council
The Conservation Section, 12 Waterloo Place, London SW1Y 4AU. Maintains a register of craftsmen

Department of the Environment
2 Marsham Street, London SW1P 3EB

Devon Rural Skills Trust
Dartmoor National Park Headquarters, Parke, Haytor Road, Bovey Tracey, Newton Abbot, Devon TQ13 9JQ

The Dry Stone Walling Association
Head Office: Young Farmers Club Centre, National Agricultural Centre, Kenilworth, Warwicks CV8 2LG. Advisory service and a newsletter

English Heritage (Historic Buildings and Monuments Commission for England)
Fortress House, 23 Savile Row, London W1X 1AB

The Georgian Group
37 Spital Square, London E1 6DY. *Secretary:* Roger White. The Group deals with the conservation and study of buildings erected 1714–1834

Geological Museum
Exhibition Road, South Kensington, London SW1. Library and identification of stone

Glass and Glazing Federation
6 Mount Row, London W1Y 6DY

Guild of Architectural Ironmongers
8 Stepney Green, London E1

Hampshire Buildings Preservation Trust Ltd
The Castle, Winchester SO23 8UE

Historic Buildings and Monuments Commission for England (HBMCE)
See *English Heritage*

Historic Buildings Council for Scotland
25 Drumsheugh Gardens, Edinburgh EH3 7RN

Historic Buildings Council for Wales
Crown Building, Cathays Park, Cardiff CF1 3NQ

Historic Farm Buildings Group
Institute of Agricultural History, Whiteknights, Reading RG6 2AG. Studies local and regional vernacular

Institute of Advanced Architectural Studies
University of York, The King's Manor, York YO1 2EP. Organizes courses on the conservation of historic buildings and post-graduate two-year courses

Ironbridge Gorge Museum Trust
Ironbridge, Telford, Shropshire TF8 7AW

Landmark Trust
Shottesbrooke, Maidenhead, Berkshire SL6 3SW. The charity rescues buildings in distress and gives them life and a future, mostly by letting them for holidays

London Master Plasterers Association
82 New Cavendish Street, London W1M 8AD

Master Thatchers Associations
See *Yellow Pages* for local MTAs or contact the Rural Development Commission. Names of thatchers and advice on thatching

Men of Stones
The Rutlands, Tinwell, Stamford, Lincs PE9 3UD

National Trust
36 Queen Anne's Gate, London SW1H 9AS

National Trust for Scotland
5 Charlotte Square, Edinburgh EH2 4DU

Natural Stone Directory
Available from Ealing Publications, Weir Bank, Bray, Maidenhead, Berkshire SL6 2ED

Royal Archaeological Institute
304 Addison House, Grove End Road, St John's Wood, London NW8 9EL

Royal Commission on Ancient Monuments in Wales
Edleston House, Queen's Road, Aberystwyth, Dyfed SY23 2HP. Concerned with the historic monuments of Wales

Royal Commission on Historical Manuscripts
Quality House, Quality Court, Chancery Lane, London WC2. Maintains National Register of Archives

Royal Commission for Historical Monuments (England)
Fortress House, 23 Savile Row, London W1X 1AB. The statutory body for the recording and study of historic buildings in England

Royal Commission on the Ancient and Historical Monuments of Scotland
54 Melville Street, Edinburgh EH3 7HF

Royal Institute of British Architects
66 Portland Place, London W1N 4AD
Bookshop, Library and Drawings Collection

The Rural Development Commission (previously CoSIRA, *Council for Small Industries in Rural Areas*)
Head Office: 141 Castle Street, Salisbury, Wiltshire SP1 3TP. See *Yellow Pages* or contact Head Office for addresses of Regional Offices

Save Britain's Heritage
68 Battersea High Street, London SW11 3HX. Conservation pressure group

Society of Architectural Historians of Great Britain
c/o HBMC London Division, Room 208, Chesham House, 30 Warwick Street, London W1R 5RD

Society for Folk Life Studies
c/o National Museum of Antiquities of Scotland, Queen Street, Edinburgh

Society for the Protection of Ancient Buildings
37 Spital Square, London E1 6DY.
Secretary: Philip Venning. The Society advises on all problems affecting old buildings, giving technical advice on their treatment and repair. Organizes annual repair courses, visits and lectures on traditional repair techniques. Publishes technical literature and a quarterly Newsletter

Stone Federation
82 New Cavendish Street, London W1N 8AD

Thirties Society
3 Park Square West, London NW1 4LJ.
Hon Secretary: Clive Aslet

Tiles and Architectural Ceramics Society
Ironbridge Gorge Museum, Telford, Shropshire TF8 7AW

Tool and Trades History Society
275 Sandridge Lane, Bromham, Chippenham, Wiltshire SN15 2JW

United Kingdom Institute for Conservation (UKIC)
The British Museum, Department of Conservation and Technical Services, London WC1B 3DG

Vernacular Architecture Group
Secretary: Mrs Barbara Hutton, 50 Daventry Close, Mickleover, Derbyshire

Victoria and Albert Museum
Conservation Department, South Kensington, London SW7 2RL

The Victorian Society
1 Priory Gardens, London W4 1TT. Concerned with the study and conservation of architecture of the Victorian and Edwardian periods

Weald and Downland Open Air Museum
Singleton, near Chichester, West Sussex

Welsh Folk Museum
St Fagans, near Cardiff.

SELECT BIBLIOGRAPHY

GENERAL WORKS

Building crafts, Vernacular architecture, Conservation and history

ASHURST, JOHN and NICOLA, *English Heritage Technical Handbooks* volumes 1 to 5, Gower Technical Press 1988

ATKINSON, TD, *Local Style in English Architecture*, Batsford 1987

BOWYER, JACK, *History of Building*, Crosby Lockwood and Staples 1973, Attic Books 1989

BOWYER, JACK, *Handbook of Building Crafts in Conservation*, Hutchinson 1981

BOWYER, JACK, *Vernacular Building Conservation*, Architectural Press 1980

BRAUN, HUGH, *Old English Houses*, Faber 1962

BRIGGS, MARTIN, *A Short History of Building Crafts*, The Clarendon Press 1925

BROWN, RJ, *The English Country Cottage*, Arrow Books 1979

BRUNSKILL, RW, *Illustrated Handbook of Vernacular Architecture*, Faber 1971, revised and expanded 1987

CLIFTON-TAYLOR, ALEC, *The Pattern of English Building*, Batsford 1962, Faber 1972

CUNNINGTON, PAMELA, *Care for Old Houses*, Prism Alpha 1984

DAVEY, NA, *A History of Building Materials*, Phoenix House 1961

FEILDEN, BERNARD M, *Conservation of Historic Buildings*, Butterworth 1982

HUGHES, PHILIP, *The Need for Old Buildings to Breathe*, SPAB Information Sheet No. 4, The Society for the Protection of Ancient Buildings 1986

INNOCENT, CF, *English Building Construction*, Cambridge University Press 1916, David and Charles 1971

INSALL, DW, *The Care of Old Buildings Today*, The Architectural Press 1973

JONES, SYDNEY R, *English Village Homes*, Batsford 1936

JOPE, EM, *Studies in Building History*, Odhams 1961

LLOYD, NATHANIEL, *History of the English House*, Architectural Press 1975, reprinted 1978

MERCER, ERIC, *English Vernacular Houses*, Royal Commission on Historical Monuments, HMSO 1975

PAIN, WILLIAM, *The Builder's Companion and Workman's General Assistant*, London 1762, reprinted Gregg International 1972

PENOYRE, JOHN and JANE, *Houses in the Landscape, A Regional Study of Vernacular Building Styles in England and Wales*, Faber 1978

POWYS, AR, *Repair of Ancient Buildings*, Dent 1929, republished by SPAB 1981 with additional notes

SALZMAN, LF, *Building in England down to 1540*, Oxford University Press 1952

WADE, JANE (editor), *Traditional Buildings in Kent*, series, 1980 onwards

WALLING

Unbaked earth and chalk walling

ALCOCK, NW, *Halford Cottages: Mud Construction*, Transactions of the Birmingham and Warwickshire Archaeological Society volume 87, 1975 pp 133–136

ASHURST, JOHN and NICOLA, *Practical Building Conservation*, English Heritage Technical Handbook volume 2: *Brick, Terracotta and Earth*, Gower Technical Press 1988

BRUNSKILL, RW, *The Clay Houses of Cumberland*, Transactions of the Ancient Monuments Society volume 10, 1962 pp 57 to 80

CLIFTON-TAYLOR, ALEC, *The Pattern of English Building*, Batsford 1962, Faber 1972

FENTON, A, *'Stone and Turf Walling'*, *Folk Life* volume 6, 1968

HARRISON, JR, *The Mud Wall in England*, Transactions of the Ancient Monuments Society volume 28, 1984

McCANN, JOHN M, *Clay and Cob Buildings*, Shire Publications 1983

NORTON, JOHN, *Building with Earth*, Intermediate Technology 1986

PEARSON, GORDON T, *Chalk; Its Use as a Structural Building Material in the County of Hampshire*, unpublished thesis for the Postgraduate Diploma in Building Conservation, Architectural Association 1982

SEABORNE, M, *Cob Cottages in Northants*, *Northamptonshire Past and Present* volume 3 No 5, 1964 pp 215–228

WALKER, B, *Clay Buildings in North-east Scotland*, Scottish Vernacular Buildings Working Group 1977

WILLIAMS ELLIS, C and J and E EASTWICK-FIELD, *'Building in Cob, Pisé and Stabilised Earth'*, *Country Life* 1947

Stone

ASHURST, JOHN and NICOLA, *Practical Building Conservation, English Heritage Technical Handbook* volume 1: *Stone Masonry*, Gower Technical Press 1988

BAGGALLAY, FRANK, *The Use of Flint in Building, especially in the County of Suffolk*, RIBA Transactions, New Series 1885 pp 105–124

BRISTOW, JC, *The Flint Industry of Brandon*, *The Architects' Journal* September 14, 1921

CAROE, ADR and MB, *Stonework: Maintenance and Surface Repair*, Council for the Care of Churches 1984

CLIFTON-TAYLOR, ALEC, *The Pattern of English Building*, Batsford 1962, Faber 1972

CLIFTON-TAYLOR, ALEC and AS IRESON, *English Stone Building*, Gollancz 1983

DAVEY, NORMAN, *Building Stones of England and Wales*, Standing Conference for Local History, Bedford Square Press 1976

FORREST, AJ, *The Masters of Flint*, Terence Dalton, Lavenham 1983

GOODALL, *'Flint Building and Walling'*, *The Architects' Journal* August 16, 1934 p 229

GREENWOOD, GB, *'English Flintwork'*, *The Builder* June 22, 1934 pp 1060–62

LEARY, ELAINE, *The Building Limestones of the British Isles*, HMSO

MASON, HJ, *Flint the Versatile Stone*, Providence Press 1978

Natural Stone Directory, Ealing Publications, Maidenhead

SHEPHERD, WALTER, *Flint: Its Origins, Properties and Uses*, Faber 1972

Brick and mathematical tiles

ASHURST, JOHN and NICOLA, *Practical Building Conservation*, English Heritage Technical Handbook volume 2: *Brick, Terracotta and Earth*, Gower Press 1988

BIDWELL, TG, *The Conservation of Brick Buildings*, Brick Development Association 1977

BRUNSKILL, RONALD and ALEC CLIFTON-TAYLOR, *English Brickwork*, Ward Locke 1977

DUCKHAM, DAVID, *Repair of Mathematical Tiles*, SPAB News, volume 5, No. 2, April 1984

DUCKHAM, DAVID, *Mathematical Tiles*, unpublished thesis for Postgraduate diploma in Building Conservation, Architectural Association 1979

EXWOOD, M, *Mathematical Tiles*, Vernacular Architecture volume 12, 1981 pp 1248–53

HAMMOND, MARTIN, *Bricks and Brickmaking*, Shire Publications 1981

HANDISYDE, CC AND BA HASELTINE, *Bricks and Brickwork*, 1975

HARLEY, LS, *A Typology of Brick*, Journal of British Archaeological Association, third series volume XXXVII, 1974 pp 63–87

LLOYD, NATHANIEL, *A History of English Brickwork*, H Greville Montgomery 1925, republished by Antique Collectors' Club 1983

SALZMAN, LF, *Building in England down to 1540*, Oxford University Press 1952

SMITH, TERENCE PAUL SMITH, *Mathematical Tiles in the Faversham Area*, The Faversham Society 1984

SMITH, TERENCE PAUL SMITH, *Refacing with Brick Tiles*, Vernacular Architecture 1979

WIGHT, JANE A, *Brick Building in England from the Middle Ages to 1550*, John Baker, London 1972

WILLIAMS, GBA, *Pointing of Stone and Brick Walling*, SPAB Technical Pamphlet No. 5, Society for the Protection of Ancient Buildings

WOODFORDE, JOHN, *Bricks to Build a House*, Routledge & Kegan 1976

Timber-framed structures

ALCOCK, NW, *Warwickshire timber-framed houses, a draft and contract, Post Medieval Archaeology* volume 9, 1975 pp 212

BRUNSKILL, RW, *Illustrated Handbook of Vernacular Architecture*, Faber 1971 and 1987

BRUNSKILL, RW, *Timber Building in Britain*, Gollancz 1985

CHARLES, FWB, with MARY CHARLES, *Conservation of Timber Buildings*, Hutchinson 1984

CHARLES, FWB, *The Timber-frame Tradition and its Preservation*, ASCHB Transactions volume 3, 1978 pp 5–28

EDLIN, HL, *Woodland Crafts in Britain*, David and Charles 1974

GOODMAN, WL, *The History of Woodworking Tools*, Bell 1964

HARRIS, RICHARD, *Discovering Timber-framed Buildings*, Shire Publications 1978

HEWETT, CECIL A, *English Historic Carpentry*, Phillimore 1980

INNOCENT, CF, *English Building Construction*, Cambridge University Press 1916, David and Charles 1971

LOCKE, PETER, *Timber Treatment – A warning about De-frassing*, and *Surface Treatment of Timber-framed Buildings*, SPAB Information Sheets 1 and 2, Society for the Protection of Ancient Buildings 1986

MERCER, E, *English Vernacular Houses*, HMSO 1975

POWYS, AR, *Repair of Ancient Buildings*, Dent 1929, republished by SPAB with additional notes 1981

REID, KENNETH, *Panel Infillings to Timber-framed Buildings*, SPAB Technical Pamphlet No. 11, The Society for the Protection of Ancient Buildings 1989

THOMAS, ANDREW, *Panel Infilling to Timber-framed Buildings*, SPAB News volume 3, No. 2, The Society for the Protection of Ancient Buildings 1982

Pargetting

BANKART, GEORGE P, *The Art of the Plaster*, Batsford 1908

BEARD, GEOFFREY, *Stucco and Decorative Plasterwork in Europe*, Thames and Hudson 1983

CARTER, ROBIN, *Pargetting*, SPAB News volume 4, No. 2, Society for the Protection of Ancient Buildings 1983

Essex County Council, No. 1: *Pargetting* 1982

Hertfordshire County Council, *Pargetting in Hertfordshire* 1983

ROOFING MATERIALS

Thatch

BROCKETT, PETER and ADELA WRIGHT, *The Care and Repair of Thatched Roofs*, SPAB Technical Pamphlet No. 10, The Society for the Protection of Ancient Buildings 1986

Council for Small Industries in Rural Areas (now the Rural Development Commission) *The Thatcher's Craft*, CoSIRA, RDA first published 1960, reprinted 1981

FENTON, A, *'Clay Building and Clay Thatch in Scotland'*, *Ulster Folklife* volumes 15/16, 1970 pp 28–51

GAILEY, RA, *'The Use of Mud in Thatching in Scotland'*, *Ulster Folklife* volume 6, 1960 pp 68–70

PETERS, JEC, *'The Solid Thatched Roof'*, *Vernacular Architecture* volume 8, 1977

SMITH, DM, *'Some Flat-Roof Thatch Survivals'*, *Folk Life* volume 16, 1978

Slate and stone

CLIFTON-TAYLOR, ALEC and AS IRESON, *English Stone Building*, Gollancz 1983

Derbyshire County Council, *Traditional Stone Roofing*

Hertfordshire County Council, *Tiles and Slates in Hertfordshire* 1984

HOLDEN, EW, *Slate Roofing in Medieval Sussex*, Sussex Archaeological Society volume 103, 1965 pp 67–78

JOPE, EM, and GG DUNNING, *'The Use of Blue Slate for Roofing in Medieval England'*, *Antiques Journal* volume 34, 1954 pp 209–17

WALTON, J, *'The English Stone-Slater's Craft'*, *Folk Life* volume 13, 1975

Shingles

STEWART, IAN, *Recovering Sompting's Spire*, SPAB News volume 5, No. 4, 1984 pp 58–60

WARD, JDU, *'Shingling – the Decline of a Craft'*, *Country Life* volume 109, Jan–June 1951 pp 316–18.

INDEX

Numerals in *italic* refer to illustrations
(see also Useful Addresses pp 161–4 and Selected Bibliography 165–8)